MW00774892

THE
CORONA
PROTOCOL

A Scientifically Proven Medical Solution to
STOP
Addiction, Bullying, Homelessness,
School Shootings and Suicide

30 years in the making

by PAUL D. CORONA, M.D.

The Corona Protocol: A Scientifically Proven Medical Solution to STOP Addiction, Bullying, Homelessness, School Shootings and Suicide. 30 years in the making by Paul D. Corona, M.D.

Hardcover: 979-8-9896000-2-1
Paperback: 979-8-9896000-1-4
eBook: 979-8-9896000-0-7
LCCN: 2024900073
Published by The Corona Protocol,
    30011 Ivy Glenn Dr., Suite 101, Laguna Niguel, CA 92677

www.drpaulcoronamd.com

Cover Design: Kathy Dunn
Author Photograph: Jackie Tran

First Printing Edition, 2024

Library of Congress Cataloguing-in-Publication
Corona, M.D., Paul D.
    The Corona Protocol: A Scientifically Proven Medical Solution to
    STOP Addiction, Bullying, Homelessness, School Shootings and
    Suicide. 30 years in the making.
    Paul D. Corona, M.D. p.312

Although this publication is designed to provide accurate information in regard to the subject matter covered, the publisher and the author assume no responsibility for errors, inaccuracies, omissions, or any other inconsistencies herein. This publication is meant as a source of valuable information for the reader, however it is not meant as a replacement for direct expert assistance. If such level of assistance is required, the services of a competent professional should be sought.

DEDICATION

In each of the previous books in this series, I have remembered those who inspired, encouraged, and supported me in my efforts to develop and communicate to as wide an audience as possible the benefits of The Corona Protocol. The list includes my family, friends, mentors, and various experts in the medical community.

Now I have the opportunity to dedicate this volume to the unsung heroes without whom none of my work could have succeeded. I am referring to my patients, whose lives are forever interwoven with mine. Your willingness to face the truth that something in your life was not working as it should, your courage to risk taking steps to get help, and your willingness to trust me to help you has made possible the remarkable life-changing results we are seeing today.

Knowing you and working together is among the greatest joys of my life. So, I dedicate this book to you and all the patients I have yet to meet because of what we have accomplished together.

Books by Paul D. Corona, M.D.:

Healing the Mind and Body : The Trilogy

Healing the Mind and Body 1
Healing the Mind and Body 2: The Doctor and Patient Guide
Healing the Mind and Body 3: The Doctor and Patient Guide

Other books in the works*

*The Corona Protocol Prescribers Guide
*The Corona Protocol: 3 Secrets to Success

TABLE OF CONTENTS

A PERSONAL NOTE FROM
DR. PAUL CORONA

I have a low tolerance for human suffering. It makes no difference whether it's a stranger or friend, a small child or elderly widow, a war veteran or schoolteacher, a patient in my office or refugees on the other side of the world, people languishing in misery concerns me. The pain I find most distressing is needless suffering.

Later, I'll tell my story. Not my entire life's story, but a critical segment appropriate of my services.

I'm an expert, trained medical doctor whose focus is relieving people's daily pain, and my profession has provided me with tools to promote healing. My immediate response to injury or illness is a fervent desire to intervene. I provide treatments that help alleviate or eliminate misery.

Of course, not all anguish can be improved or evaded. Everyone experiences heartbreaking losses, soreness, muscle aches, lacerations (from a paper cut to a wound requiring stitches), and abrasions.

Some have broken a bone, live with disabilities or navigate chronic illnesses. Life-saving surgeries require periods of rehabilitation.

I cannot sit by idly when it comes to unnecessary misery. I share my passion for helping others and hope you feel the same. There are remedies for people in pain. I want to see others get help. If you are a family physician and want to do more for your patients to promote their well-being, this book is for you. If you are someone suffering depression or has been diagnosed with PTSD and have yet to find the help you need, *this book is for you.*

If you have a family member or friend with debilitating anxiety, depression, or bipolar disorder, this book is for you. Many wake every morning dreading feeling sad, overwhelmed, afraid, inadequate, and angry. These thoughts torture them, and they can become confused by their behavior. Perhaps they hang on, hoping for a cure to relieve their feelings.

What They Don't Know Is a Solution Exists.

Over the last thirty years, neuroscience research has repeatedly shown the mind and body function as one complete system. Physiology and psychology function together in an unbreakable link. The same nervous system running the body and registering pain also churns out thoughts, feelings, and emotions. People can't suffer a chronic physical illness without their moods being affected. It's equally impossible to struggle with a mood disorder without it affecting their health and social life. Progress toward resolving mood disorders requires a collaboration of healthcare professionals, including primary family physicians, psychiatrists, psychologists, nurse practitioners, physician assistants, and patients. We should add the roles alternative and holistic practitioners play.

I find collaboration with colleagues and other healthcare professionals a rewarding aspect of my practice. The value of our combined knowledge, experience, and skill enables us to tackle mood disorder cases far too complex for a single, specialized practitioner.

A family physician is often the first contact to evaluate and diagnose a mood disorder. Optimally, they can treat both emotional and physical aspects since their training includes both. Primary care providers, including PAs and NPs, tend to be friendlier, have excellent communication skills, and are good listeners.

We care about what we do and the people we care for. We get to know each other and often go on to treat their families and friends. Treating the whole community creates a domino effect. Healing one person leads to healing others. It's exciting to change and improve so many lives.

I Urge Practitioners to Explore Incorporating This Protocol into Their Practices.

Many patients hesitate to see a "shrink" because of the cultural stigma still attached to psychotherapy.

Patients often say, "Look, Doctor, I just feel unhappy, doomed, and hopeless all the time, but I'm not crazy."

Sadly, there are family practice physicians who don't realize they can treat mood disorders when symptoms first appear before they refer them to a psychologist or other specialist.

Over time, I hope every family physician will appreciate the steps they can take to resolve mood disorders, developing the necessary skills and confidence to treat the body and mind. To do so, they'll need more than a thorough knowledge of available medications, or what pharmaceutical brochures and sales reps claim about their medications.

They'll need a rational approach for diagnosing specific causes of the complaints, and for determining the medication most likely to produce the best results, quickly.

This is the essence of the Corona Protocol.

MY JOURNEY

When registering for pre-med courses, I wasn't planning a future where I'd treat mood disorders. Like most of my colleagues in the medical profession, my deepest desire was to work at improving the health of my patients by addressing physical complaints with organic causes such as illness, injury, organ malfunction, embolism, and more.

Over many years of family practice, I discovered nearly eighty percent of my patients' complaints were caused or exacerbated by "emotional" issues. I place quotation marks around emotional because emotions are not imaginary or unreal; they arise from neurological brain activity.

The remarkable number of patients who struggled from increased stress, worry, or fear from a physical complaint, and how well they were prepared to respond to it logistically, financially, etcetera, rose to a figure closer to one hundred percent.

Once I turned my attention to the underlying neurological factors in health care, I saw remarkable changes in my patients. Even those with illnesses for which modern medicine has no known cure, such as fibromyalgia, showed marked improvement in their attitudes in dealing with their ailments and their lives. Their complaints diminished and, in many cases, were fully resolved.

No choice presented itself to me other than an aggressive pursuit of the best treatment for these crucial threats to human health and happiness.

The further I went, the more I learned, and the more my patients received help from my research and practice. While moving forward, I now appreciate occasional setbacks, as I've learned from them as much as or sometimes more than I have from my successes. These realizations evolved into a rational approach to treating mood disorders: The Corona Protocol.

The Corona Protocol differs from the standard procedure of prescribing a well-known or trendy antidepressant to patients whose symptoms indicate a mood disorder.

If patients don't display improvement within a month or two, a second prescription is written for a higher dosage. This may snowball into a higher dosage that still doesn't work before the doctor decides to wean the patient off. Then they try a new medication. Some patients suffer for six months or more before they experience any benefit—if they last that long. Few patients with anxiety or depressive disorders have the stamina to wait so long for relief, especially when the unwanted side effects of each medication are too much. No wonder some patients feel like they've been their doctor's lab rats.

There are other problems with this approach, including the innumerable chemical variations differentiating patients. These specifics decide the effectiveness of a medication and how well its side effects can be tolerated. When doctors without much knowledge about their patients prescribe from the wide variety of drugs available for treating mood disorders, they're rolling the dice in hope of a favorable outcome.

* * *

At its core, the Corona Protocol is an evidence-based, rational approach to health care.

The first step of the protocol is a differential diagnosis, which includes a complete physical, and, in some cases, consulting with other specialists who've worked with and know the patient well.

The second step is an intense focus on the patient's family history, which is more extensive than what a family physician typically performs. The Corona Protocol doesn't allow the patient's doctor to skim over the family history. They must study it carefully.

This provides one of many clues that support choosing the wrong or suboptimal medication. The goal is to come as close as possible to the best medication for each person from the start. Family history is indispensable because genetic predispositions indicate likely neurochemical culprits needing our attention. No shortcuts can be taken. The better a doctor understands what's happening in the patient's brain chemistry, the more precisely they're able to choose a matching psychotropic medication with the most potential.

The same "close look" approach is applied to the patient's personal history. I note each emotional and physical symptom and any stressors. During visits, details are tracked by dictating and keeping detailed notes to ensure symptoms are all resolved.

Mood disorders tend to overlap. For example, an anxious person may experience bouts of depression. A depressive patient may be tortured by repetitive, dark thoughts that can torture him or her to the point where they feel hopeless and worse. The doctor must be well-informed to decide whether the complaint is stress and mood related or something else.

Stories of unhealthy home environments, abuse, trauma, at-risk adolescent behavior, and more enable the physician to clarify the diagnosis. The more accurate the diagnosis, the more rational a choice in prescribing medication.

The first goal of the Corona Protocol is to ensure the first medication prescribed is the best and most effective. It's crucial to build a strong foundation. We depend on clear and proven reasons for each step to treat mood disorders.

Adjusting brain neurochemistry is a moving target. Everyone's body chemistry changes over time. Hormone levels increase and decrease. Adrenals respond to stress and other factors. The goal isn't reached easily, nor consistently attained. Having a rational, consistent process produces better results than blindly writing prescriptions.

The Corona Protocol was crafted over the course of a career dedicated to helping individuals facing not just the challenges of their disorders, but also the additional burdens of misunderstanding and mistreatment from family and friends due to these hidden illnesses. Conditions with visible wounds or readily recognizable symptoms, like high fever or detectable cancers on X-rays, receive the attention they deserve. However, it's only with conditions like mood disorders where individuals often hear dismissive comments such as, "It's all in your head," implying their illness is merely imagined.

Unfortunately, some people assume this is what psychosomatic means: an imagined illness that can be brought under control by the patient. The Corona Protocol, however, takes the "psycho" out of psychosomatic. Or rather, we stress the authentic connection between the mind and body—the true essence of the word psychosomatic.

By doing so, we help those suffering understand the biological source of their misery during the most challenging time of their lives. We assure them that having this disorder is not their fault. They don't have to pretend to be okay and avoid seeking professional help just because society judges them as a "crazy" person.

We encourage family and friends to back off with well-intended but useless comments while enlightening them about the reality of the patient's misery.

Though Western Medicine has come a long way, the Corona Protocol adds another branch, solidly rooted in traditional and clinical standards. We've been rewarded by the remarkable number of patients and family members telling us we've given them their lives back.

It's been gratifying observing a variety of complaints resolved in our office when certain disorders or severe physical symptoms haven't responded to the intervention of other practitioners and specialists but have seen results through our protocols.

Like many others who've been willing to do whatever it takes to pursue their vision, my journey has been challenging. At times, it's been like a roller coaster, and during other times, a lonely journey.

The refreshed, motivated version of me only appeared over the last several years. It took place after other physicians and psychiatrists agreed and supported my approach to resolving mood disorders and other medical conditions. Some of my colleagues have seen the effectiveness of the Corona Protocol after referring patients to our office as a last resort.

If you're open to finding and learning a new method, I will take you on an exciting voyage, encompassing the essence of healing, the rebirth of dead hopes, and a newfound love for life. We'll explore the true meaning of the mind-body connection.

Learning to heal the mind and body brings miraculous results.

I owe immense gratitude to my many patients for their willingness to follow the Corona Protocol. These men, women, and children are why I've fought and do the work.

Access to the Corona Protocol is my deepest desire. I hope people will have hope they'll be healed. The method is for you if you want to witness powerful results by completely treating the mind and body. Practitioners with compassion and empathy will be moved to learn the protocol and acquire and share a fuller understanding of a new face in medicine, one developed from out-of-the-box thinking, creativity, and innovative science.

I present this protocol to you hoping you'll heed the call to action. I hope family physicians meet the challenge and address their patients' mental health and physical wellbeing, one where many hopeless, suffering patients will experience relief. No one can provide an absolute guarantee for all mental health issues, but I'm optimistic we can treat a significant amount of bleakness, pain, and suffering. Our world can shine brighter and become happier. Suffering isn't necessary, nor does it need to go undiagnosed and untreated. Why? Because the Corona Protocol works.

Many blessings to you and your loved ones.

–Dr. Paul, M.D.

PART ONE

Disruptive Disorders

In this opening chapter, we cover the four most common conditions I diagnose and treat. The first and most common problems I see are anxiety disorders.

CHAPTER 1

Anxiety Disorders

It's challenging separating anxiety and depression because they can go hand-in-hand. Anxiety is commonly associated with pain and other somatic (physical) symptoms. Such acute symptoms can cause persistent or chronically recurring indications and are disruptive to one's life. The Mind-Body connection is vastly underappreciated by society and most physicians, including psychiatrists.

Some don't like the term "anxiety" but can relate more to the word "stress." They may not understand that they are having symptoms of anxiety-related exposure to stressful situations and the disruption this causes in one's life. We are all exposed to stress, some more than others, and some can manage it better. Others cannot.

There is also a difference between good stress and bad stress.

FURTHER READING:

For more information about this topic, check out my second book, Chapter 3, Managing Stress. It includes a guided meditation by pastor and editor extraordinaire, Chuck Smith Jr.

There are many types of anxiety disorders.

You can learn more in my second book, chapter 4, and in the 12-part series covering the subject on my podcast, The Dr. Paul Show.

IMPORTANT NOTE:

All patient names are fictional to ensure their privacy. The only exceptions would be those patients who have volunteered testimonials and have given permission to use only their first names.

Most of the case stories (I prefer this term to the more medical term case *studies*) I will share with you are based on the stories of patients I've seen in my practice. Their names and some details have been changed to protect their identity and respect their privacy.

Katie

I first saw Katie when she was 17 years old when she was a junior in high school. She was referred to me by her psychologist Kim after seeing her for the previous year. She was raised in a healthy environment with her parents involved in her life. "She's had problems with anxiety since she was five when we lost our dog," her father said. It'd been the first time she'd experienced a significant loss. The incident deeply affected her emotionally and mentally.

Her parents noticed her increased anxiousness, especially when she went to kindergarten. "She has separation anxiety when I drop her off. She screams for me when I leave," her mother said. Over time, things improved, but Katie still felt nervous without a parent or grandparent present.

In elementary school, Katie was often nervous and shy, sometimes with those close to her. She'd involuntarily tap her lower legs. On occasion, the school nurse called her mother to pick her up for bad stomachaches and/or headaches. The pediatrician said Katie was fine. It was, "Just stress."

During middle school, things worsened. Anxiety increased and brought on more symptoms such as anxiety attacks, shortness of breath, racing of the heart, sweating, shakiness, and nausea. Katie developed headaches, neck, shoulder, and upper back tightness and pain.

Her dentist noticed symptoms of her clenching her jaw at night, grinding down her teeth. She was prescribed to wear a night guard.

Katie had difficulty falling asleep due to worrying about what happened during the day and what might happen the next day. She suffered difficulty shutting her brain down.

Her school psychologist evaluated her. He discussed ways to relieve stress, including proper breathing techniques and suggesting adopting some type of regular exercise. He met with her to address her frequent and unremitting anxiety. She stopped going because she felt it wasn't helping.

At 16, she saw a new psychotherapist: Kim. I've worked with her for many years. She connected well with Katie, and they made progress by learning coping skills and maximizing stress reduction techniques.

However, Kim recognized a deeper problem and referred her to me to assess the medical aspects. Kim was concerned that Katie was having suicidal ideation but assured the psychologist and me she'd not follow through.

When asked, Katie said, "It scares me that I'm thinking about it."

Katie also frequently wore a face mask, even when outside and away from others. "I don't want to get the virus and die a slow, painful death."

"Don't watch the news," her parents said. "It's just making you more anxious and afraid."

For our first session, we met one on one. Later, we brought in her parents to review my findings and recommendations. Katie confided she was getting Xanax and Klonopin from friends to relieve her anxiety, but she also felt sedated and foggy.

She took a pill while drinking at a party. "I almost passed out," she said.

I agreed to keep the incident between us, being sure to get her word she'd not do so again. "It's dangerous mixing tranquilizers with alcohol," I said. "So many street drugs are laced with fentanyl, which can lead to sudden death."

She knew about the drug epidemic, which scared her. She agreed to my treatment plan.

I only break confidentiality if I feel my patient is at risk of harming himself or herself, or someone else. It's essential patients give me their word in a verbal contract that they'll not harm themselves and will notify me if any planning thoughts occur.

Her mother revealed she and her mother, Katie's grandmother, each suffered from anxiety. They were hesitant about medications, which is common. Our society has an unreasonably strong anti-medication mentality. Some find it difficult to consider that mood disorders are not just psychological or mental, but also physical and neurological.

The brain is an organ just like any other. I argue it's the most important one. Just because we can't measure neurochemical imbalances with lab tests and scanning doesn't mean they aren't real.

Katie's parents brought up her age: she wasn't yet 18. They read certain medications were only approved for patients 18 and older.

"It's important not to get information from the internet, any governmental body, or family and friends. It can be extremely confusing and misleading," I told them. "The medications I use are safe for teenagers and younger children when they are appropriate. They work. I don't like to discriminate based on age. I want my patients to get better no matter how old they are."

They agreed to try an SNRI: a medication that balances serotonin and norepinephrine at the same time. I explained that much of what they have learned about antidepressants is untrue. They are extremely safe when given to the right person for the correct diagnosis. Antidepressants, especially the SNRI class, are often the best treatment for anxiety disorders.

In addition to the myth that they're dangerous, it's also false they take weeks or months to work. They typically work within a few days to a week, and within two weeks at most. There are no dangerous side effects. If there are any side effects, they are typically mild and passing. Significant side effects lead to stopping the offending medication. We only know they'll work by using a rational trial and error approach alongside the most cutting-edge treatment available for mental and physical disorders.

I reviewed her breathing techniques and other forms of stress reduction, including continuing her psychologist's recommended regular exercise program.

"Call me after the first week" I said, "which is the usual time it takes to know if we're on the right track."

When she called, she reported doing significantly better. Her physical symptoms had improved. She slept better and saw a dramatic reduction in her anxiety.

What I love most about this job is seeing such dramatic results.

Katie and her parents shared with me how well she was doing again at the next follow-up visit. She was significantly better than the first. Her anxiety and physical symptoms had almost completely resolved. She slept better, had more daytime energy, focused better on school, and wasn't overwhelmed with the stressors of being a teenager.

"Do you feel like you're back to your old self?" I asked.

"To be honest? I wish I'd felt like this months ago," she said.

A month later, she felt even better as life settled and opened up.

I shared with Katie and her parents the true statistics and science about my namesake virus, which reassured them. I referred them to several The Dr. Paul Show podcasts as they were interested in more details about the topic. I also recommended good supportive supplements scientifically proven to reduce risk.

Katie is still a patient to this day and will have a much better senior year of high school, as well as the rest of her life.

Comments:

Katie's was a typical case. Showing symptoms as a child was significant, as they will often worsen with age. Experiencing separation anxiety from her mother, which built on her fear of loss when their beloved dog died, was another clue.

Her experience worsened during and after puberty, which is extremely common. Even without childhood onset, problems with mood, such as anxiety, can be present in middle school. It sometimes gets better or worse during high school and later in life.

The lack of significant stressors didn't make a difference for Katie. They would have made it worse. Often, anxiety doesn't make sense. People focus on outside stress rather than the stress happening within them.

This type of quick and easy resolution of problems always brings a smile to my face and joy from deep inside me. I love helping children and teenagers because doing so alters the rest of their lives for the better.

My choice of prescribing an SNRI goes against the grain. A pervasive myth in psychiatry is that SSRIs (medications that only balance serotonin) are the best first-line choices. I've disagreed for almost 30 years.

SNRIs are the best first-line choices. SSRIs take second place. This is especially true when anxiety and/or physical/somatic symptoms exist.

FURTHER READING:

For more information about the different classes of psychotropic medications, check out chapter 3. I also talk about medications throughout my three-book series *Healing the Mind and Body: The Trilogy* (Corona, 2014).

Jim

Jim was referred to me by a friend who is also one of my patients. He sought help for his worsening anxiety, which had begun to significantly impact his life. Jim had a reserved upbringing in a reasonably healthy household, devoid of any notable abuse. However, his anxiety escalated during 5th grade when his parents separated and divorced.

Throughout middle school and high school, Jim resorted to self-medicating with food, which led to a substantial weight gain. He faced teasing about his weight during middle school. The situation escalated in high school, causing him to isolate himself and minimize contact with others. While he had a few close friends he'd hang out with, he preferred to stay home in his room, playing video games and connecting with people on the Internet.

Jim wasn't fond of sports and felt uncomfortable around popular athletes due to his weight and low self-esteem.

When I met Jim at the age of 28, he worked as a deli driver for a private mail service. He'd developed a fear of driving over the prior year. His fear had intensified due to his exposure to accidents on the road, given his extensive time spent driving. He experienced a car accident when his vehicle was struck on the side by another driver. Although he didn't sustain any significant injuries, it didn't bother him until the following year.

Nothing notable happened the previous year to explain why his anxiety increased. I pointed out it'd been the same time the pandemic started.

He realized it'd been when he heard news reports and felt panicked about what he heard. "The old man I see on TV all the time seems so nice and seems to know what he's talking about, right?" he asked.

Since his job involved delivering packages, he was afraid he'd catch the virus. The packages could be contaminated, so he wore gloves and a mask everywhere. He'd change gloves frequently as he handled packages. He tried avoiding people he delivered to by leaving the packages and knocking when a signature was required. He wore his mask while driving, convinced people were staring, pointing, and laughing at him.

Jim couldn't figure out why he was afraid of driving. Other cars seemed to be going faster than he remembered. Jim was afraid of getting into an accident, which would result in having to stop and being exposed to others. Jim tried to stay in the right lane of the freeway and took to the side streets. Doing so caused him to take more time to deliver the packages. Some packages arrived late, and he worked past dark trying to get all his work done.

Jim's boss questioned what was going on. "Why are you taking so long with deliveries?"

He was afraid he might lose his job if his performance did not improve. Jim didn't understand. He was a safe driver. "Why am I afraid of doing something I've been doing for years without being scared until now?"

Soon, Jim developed symptoms of anxiety, such as difficulty falling asleep, and staying asleep when he could. His neck, shoulders and upper back hurt and grew stiff. He developed lower back pain, stomach aches, and difficulty focusing and staying on task. His anxiety intensified at night. "It doesn't make sense. I'm home in my safe space."

He unwound by drinking beer during the workweek, something he previously saved for weekends and evenings when he didn't work the next day. He drank more to wind down and get some sleep. Soon, he added vodka. It worked better.

Jim continued his years-long pattern of overeating, drawn to sugars and carbohydrates. He'd been overweight since middle school. His weight gain worsened during adulthood as his habits continued.

He shared the truth that his father and paternal grandfather had also struggled with anxiety. It had led to problematic drinking and unhealthy lifestyles for them, as well.

"You can't rationalize the state of anxiety. For example, lots of people are afraid of flying. Meanwhile, statistics prove that flying is the safest form of transportation," I told him.

"I'm not sure," Jim said. "Flying still makes me nervous. I'm not crazy about being in a long metal tube speeding through the sky, strapped to a seat."

"You can't get ahead of this and figure it out because it's something you can't control," I explained. "You'd benefit from regular exercise, starting with a walking program. Add some diaphragmatic breathing techniques. Check out other ways to learn how to relax like meditation and yoga. I'd also like to prescribe you an SNRI."

"My family doctor put me on one of those last year," Jim said. "It helped the anxiety, but I felt flat, apathetic, and tired all the time."

"There are better medicines now. I'd like you to give it a shot."

"Sure," he said. "I'm open."

"I have one I think will be the perfect fit."

We had a follow-up phone call appointment several days later. "I'm already feeling a little better after a week," he said. "But not much."

"I'm sleeping better at night, though there's still some insomnia. But my neck and back aches are about half as bad and I'm not eating as much bad stuff at night."

Some symptoms of anxiety remained; he still couldn't completely stop eating in the evening.

The perfect next piece of the puzzle would be Topamax, a product I have prescribed for 30 years. The medicine balances GABA (Gamma Aminobutyric Acid). Its main benefits are a reduction in anxiety, pain, and other somatic symptoms. Topamax also helps with appetite, especially cravings for sugars and carbohydrates when people seek to "stress eat" through "comfort foods." It's well known for migraine treatment, but its other off-label benefits are exciting to witness.

"I'd like to explain the titration schedule," I told Jim. "You'll take the medication after work and before eating in the evening."

Jim didn't see a significant difference during the first week, which is typical. After the second week, I knew the dose was too low. I called in a higher dose and explained how to titrate the dose higher until our next visit two weeks later.

Such outcomes no longer surprise me. When it works, the results still bring me joy. Jim followed up. He was smiling and seemed much more relaxed. "My anxiety is entirely gone. I'm not afraid of germs or driving. My boss is happy I'm back to my old self. Other people are telling me I look better physically and emotionally."

His physical symptoms, such as neck and back pain, stomach aches, and acid reflux had improved. His body felt better. He lost a significant amount of weight. He stopped drinking alcohol during the workweek and only occasionally on the weekends; if even that, which was much less than before.

"Alcohol is made up of liquid sugar and carbohydrates," I said. "Your medication works for the liquid and solid varieties of the good stuff."

"I don't feel the need to drink to wind down at night now. My appetite's gone down a lot, too," Jim said.

"The medicine reduces the desire to drink carbonated beverages, which is why you may not like drinking sodas anymore. It alters the taste of carbonated beverages and takes away the fizz, making them taste flat, like they've been sitting out too long." This side effect irritates some people, though many realize sodas are not great for you. It makes it easier to stop drinking them if they wish.

He noticed beer was a little flat, though he still liked it, just much less of it. He craved more proteins, vegetables, and fruits. He kept carbs and sugars to a minimum when those types of food were readily available.

After some tweaking of Jim's medications and augmentation, he ended up feeling great. "It's like I'm a new person. I'm excited about the future. I don't feel crippled by anxiety anymore like I've had most of my life."

He lost weight properly over the following months by increasing cardiovascular exercise and resistance training along with adopting healthy eating habits.

Jim found himself in a relationship, which was going quite well. His anxiety and low self-esteem had held him back in his connections with others, especially women. Things changed. People who knew him spotted his new confidence.

It also helped assuage his fears when I shared the real science and statistics in 2021 and 2022 about the pandemic and the public health agencies response.

The key issue to remember about psychotropic medications is they're healthy and holistic. The correct psychotropic medications help the person stay in control rather than controlling the person.

They help the body heal itself. They rebalance neurochemicals that go out of balance for reasons the person can't control. Psychotropic medications specifically fix the source of the problem, not just the symptoms. Symptomatic medications can be good Band-Aids, but they don't fix or cure the problem. The goal for each of my patients is complete remission, which means being completely well in both mind and body.

FURTHER READING:

Regarding the psychotropic medications I work with, check out book three in my trilogy *Healing the Mind and Body* series.

There's a chapter that covers all the medications in detail. These medications worked well for Jim because they balance the two most essential neurochemicals related to anxiety (as well as physical symptoms), which are norepinephrine and GABA, with serotonin taking third place.

CHAPTER 2

Depression

Depression is the second most common mental illness I diagnose and treat. As is the case with anxiety, depression also presents in many different ways. From Major Depressive Disorder to mild variations such as dysthymia and other minor variants, they can all be quite affecting and disabling.

It's common for anxiety to be another factor, but one often predominates. Treatment of one can improve the condition of the other.

You cannot separate the body and mind since both are intimately connected.

Whereas anxiety disorders are characterized by anxiety attacks, panic attacks, somatic/physical symptoms, insomnia etc., depression presents in other ways. Examples are fatigue, low motivation and energy, frequent sadness, crying easily, feelings of hopelessness, helplessness, worthlessness, despair, and suicidal ideation.

Depression is substantial if it leads to anhedonia, which means a lack of interest in things the person typically loves to do but suddenly finds too much of a chore and thus avoids. Anhedonia is the most specific and sensitive symptom that designates the diagnosis of depression, along with depressed mood.

Many don't understand the true meaning of depression. There's a misperception that the person is weak and can't handle life.

Like other mood disorders, it's difficult for many to perceive depression as a medical problem with real medical solutions. Many struggle with accepting the diagnosis, especially for men, who often feel having depression is an assault on their machismo and projects weakness. That's not to say women don't struggle with the diagnosis, as they sure do.

For all patients, I emphasize to them that depression isn't their fault. There's a scientific protocol that works better than they can imagine.

FURTHER READING:

Depression is misunderstood, which I explained in chapter 10 of my first book, "The D Word." I also discuss depression throughout my books and podcasts if you would like more detailed information about the topic.

Molly

Molly's family doctor referred her to me to take over her care.

At 42 years old, she worked as a restaurant manager before forced to close due to the pandemic. She'd been out of work for several months when I saw her. She was collecting unemployment.

She displayed a long history of depression and anxiety. It worsened since being laid off. Molly isolated herself for months and never ventured out.

Molly spent most of her time in her room, sleeping, watching TV, and scrolling through social media. She ate more than usual. She gained weight since her activities were reduced, becoming miserable and embarrassed about her appearance. It was obvious she hadn't been taking proper care of herself.

The first order of business was a psychiatric evaluation. Reviewing her complete history, as is done with each new patient, starting from childhood, I assessed each stage in her life.

As a teenager, she struggled with depression. She saw a counselor but improved after high school during her 20s. "I always had irritability and depression-like symptoms for a few days before my menstrual cycle, but it always got better," she shared.

Molly married in her late 20s and had two children over the following five years. After her first pregnancy, she felt depressed during the first month. It lasted six months before getting better. She was offered an antidepressant but decided against it. "I don't want to be on a daily medication." She believed she'd get better on her own.

She felt fantastic while pregnant with her second child. People commented how she looked so healthy and had the "pregnancy glow."

Her situation changed after the second delivery. The depression was more severe and lasted longer. Her husband and friends were concerned; she just wasn't her normal self.

Her obstetrician talked her into trying a medication and gave her an SSRI. She felt better, but didn't like the sexual side effects, despite feeling in the mood.

After a few months, she went off her medicines and felt better than before, but never got back to her baseline. "I wanted to feel like my old self."

Things were going okay until six years later. Her husband told her he wanted to separate to have some space. He agreed to split duty with the kids and split the finances. Of course, Molly was stunned and hurt. She asked if he was seeing someone, which he denied. It wasn't true. Devastated, Molly blamed herself, believing her recurring depression and mood swings drove him away. She hadn't been herself, wasn't acting right, and was sure he was tired of it and just wanted to move on.

She thought their marriage vows would mean more and he'd stay with her through their most challenging times. "At least," she told me, "That's how it's supposed to happen in fairytales."

Molly came to my office again after experiencing more sadness, irritability, and fatigue for as long as two weeks before her menstrual cycle.

This is often the case for women during their late 30s to early 40s. Her primary care doctor and OB/GYN urged her to try an antidepressant, but she felt she could do it on her own. Molly exercised more and ate better, thinking if she lost weight and got in shape her estranged husband would fall in love with her again.

Over time, she understood that was unlikely and lost her motivation to get healthy.

Molly lost her job because of the pandemic. She had little drive to go out, preferring to stay home. Her kids were concerned because they wanted their mother back and felt she was not involved in their lives. Even though the kids were home learning remotely, she showed little interest in their schoolwork or their social lives.

A friend told her about some job opportunities, but she wasn't interested. She collected unemployment and didn't feel like working.

Molly suffered frequent crying spells, which she tried to suppress. She didn't want her kids to see her at her lowest. They did.

Tossing and turning at night, she slept most of the day. There wasn't a reason to get up; she had nothing important to do. Life felt hopeless, and she felt worthless. She didn't shower daily and kept the same clothes on when she wasn't wearing pajamas.

Molly was embarrassed to admit having suicidal thoughts but assured me she'd never put her kids through such a tragedy. The fact she believed so was significant.

Her family history impacted her life. Molly's mother also suffered from depression. Her father was an alcoholic with severe anger issues. I found more evidence of mood disorders while exploring her family history.

Since she had a lot of negative thoughts about psychotropic medications from having taken one briefly, it took effort to convince her to treat her condition in a rational, medical way. Thankfully, I convinced her. Here's how.

I explained everything in visual terms. I drew two neurons (nerve cells) and showed how they communicate. Psychotropic medications work by forcing specific neurochemicals to move in the right direction.

"I'm going to start by boosting your dopamine level and norepinephrines. I'm prescribing Wellbutrin XL," I said.

Molly titrated it over the following week and called for her one-week follow-up. She felt significantly better, energy and motivation-wise. "I think my depression is lifting somewhat," she said. "I'm having better focus and concentration. My memory's improved. I can't believe the difference."

She ventured out more and started a walking program. Her kids were relieved to see her smile and show interest in them. Their mother was coming back to life.

We weren't done yet. Molly still felt she was worrying about the past and future rather than being in the moment. She still wasn't sleeping great, though she was happy her energy increased. She still experienced recurring depression and irritability a couple of weeks before her menstrual cycle. I added an SSRI. Within a couple of weeks of titrating the dose, she couldn't believe how much better she was feeling.

The premenstrual symptoms faded. I shared the trick of doubling the dose on symptomatic premenstrual days. Doing so often resolves the extra symptoms. She slept better, too, and wasn't worrying as much. Molly felt more hopeful about the future.

She was thrilled when the restaurant reopened and hired her again, only this time as manager. Molly didn't dream she'd go back but was on the path of positivity and liveliness. During follow-up visits, I didn't need to change the doses and kept her on the same combination. She's in full remission: another life restored.

Comments:

Molly's story is much like many I have experienced in my chosen field. She has all the factors necessary to culminate in a mood disorder. The first piece is having strong genetics as her lineage also suffered depressive episodes, even when life was going well for them.

The second part was her having a strong hormonal component. This started after puberty, continued premenstrually PMS, or more appropriately, PMDD, and worsened after childbirth. Typically, depression gets worse after each childbirth. If Molly had more children, it would've gotten continuously worse. The good news is if we find out what worked previously, it's more likely the same medications will work again.

It's also hopeful for women like Molly in that they'd be able to continue the medications during the pregnancy if needed. Most psychotropic medications are safe during this time.

The next time situations might worsen is during pre-perimenopause. I've seen these changes start in the late 30s to early 40s.

After that, the next time of dramatic change happens during full-blown menopause when menstrual cycles stop, hot flashes worsen, and moods crash.

I chose an SSRI rather than an SNRI because her symptoms seemed to be related to an imbalance of serotonin due to the menstrual component, lack of somatic symptoms and severe anxiety. Unless the SSRI worked well, I would've switched her to an SNRI to see if it could've worked better.

The third most crucial factor is situational stressors, which she definitely had. She lost her marriage and became miserable to the point where she wanted to give up on life. She lost the job she loved, which gave her an identity as a functioning and vital person. She had the "perfect storm" — when all the worst factors come together at once.

Molly's situation led to her getting stuck in a mood disorder she couldn't get out of. It's important to point out to patients it's not their fault. They're not weak. It takes strength to seek help, making it to the other side and becoming a happy, functional human being.

Glenn

After being referred to me by a work friend and patient, Glenn was reluctant to see me because he'd grown used to how he felt and didn't know better. He didn't think he had a problem. At 48, he worked as a computer engineer. During the pandemic, his company closed its office, forcing the employees to work remotely. Doing so didn't faze him; Glenn was glad. He liked being alone.

Once the company opened, employees were allowed to return. Glenn petitioned his boss to let him stay home. His boss agreed, citing his productivity, if he matched the results.

His friends grew worried. Glenn was quiet and shy but withdrew and wouldn't answer any calls.

Worried about contracting the virus, Glenn avoided people. He was physically healthy and had no risk factors if he ended up getting infected. His friends persisted until he agreed to get help from me.

I reviewed his intake form. Glenn was raised in a strict household. His father sometimes got violent with him and his siblings, especially when drinking.

Glenn's mother was passive and didn't step in to protect them. They grew up afraid of him and tried to stay away from him as much as possible. He grew up shy and quiet, with few friends. He did well in school but was teased for being shy, awkward, and a nerd for having high grades.

In college, he studied computer engineering. He preferred college: others let him be. He spent most of his time in his room or the library and had no close friends.

During vacations, he found excuses not to go home. Even though his father was no longer violent, he carried resentments for what his family went through.

Glenn had brief relationships with women, none of them serious. He felt more comfortable on his own. He never married or had children.

On review of his symptoms, he suffered neck and shoulder tension and lower back pain, which he attributed to sitting for hours at the computer. He didn't like exercising, which required going out and possibly seeing other people, which he avoided. He would have occasional cramping, bloating, and acid reflux, which he blamed on his poor eating habits.

He fell asleep easily at night but would wake in the middle of the night. "I have a lot of trouble falling asleep again," he said. "My mind's always racing, thinking about what I have to do the next day."

He didn't smile the entire visit, nor did he make much eye contact. Glenn denied having suicidal thoughts, and I didn't detect any history of cycling of his mood or of mania, or other signs of instability.

Glenn started an SNRI since he had somatic symptoms. Serotonin is often involved in depression and anxiety disorders, so the first choice is usually between an SSRI and an SNRI. Usually, the latter is better, which goes against the grain. Most prescribers, whether primary care or psychiatrists, prefer subscribing SSRIs first.

Responding well over the next 1 to 2 weeks, his neck, shoulder, and back pain significantly improved. His stomach and intestines felt better, and he slept through the night. He was quite surprised since he hadn't understood he was depressed and didn't realize it was a medical/chemical problem.

Even though he was feeling better, I could tell he'd benefit from Wellbutrin XL, balancing norepinephrine a little more. The medicine's attribute is boosting dopamine, which increases energy and motivation. I refer to the SNRI-Wellbutrin XL combination as "the Dynamic Duo" of psychotropic medications.

I was surprised when I saw him smile for periods of our follow-up visit.

He ventured out occasionally, going to the store instead of having everything delivered. He made better food choices. They were surprised at work when he visited his coworkers and attended meetings.

His friends were thrilled. The one who referred him called to thank me for what I'd done for him.

Glenn said, "I never understood what depression was because I've felt this way for as long as I could remember. I didn't think that would ever change."

"That was the old normal and now you need to get used to the new normal," I said.

"I'm glad I was treated. I legit feel like I have a new lease on life," Glenn said.

"Your story, and others like yours are the reason I love this job so much," I admitted.

Comments:

In Glenn's case, certain factors led to his depression. There was obviously a family history with his father, and he suspected that his mother had depression. Also, his upbringing was turbulent. He sustained physical and emotional abuse, as well as neglect from both parents. He was socially awkward and was teased at school.

I surmised he had a mild form of Asperger's syndrome, which is on the autistic spectrum. Some clues? Glenn was awkward and often missed social cues. He lacked significant personal relationships. His profession as an engineer was also a clue.

Treating his depression improved his quality of life so much that the autistic spectrum was more in the background and became insignificant.

The results were satisfying for me because this was a complete surprise to him. I really enjoy seeing my patients thrive and as their loved ones witness their transformation firsthand.

Glenn didn't realize he had a chemical imbalance, nor did he know there was a medical answer to a state he found normal and could fix.

When I see these results, it makes me happy, but also sad. It reminds me of how many people need help who aren't receiving it. There are so many people in despair, and so many more that never get the care they need. I plan to do my best to change that.

CHAPTER 3

Bipolar Disorder

Bipolar disorder is one of my favorite conditions to treat, as it presents a unique challenge. I find immense satisfaction in witnessing dramatic improvements firsthand when this condition is properly addressed. Bipolar disorder is still one of the most underdiagnosed, undertreated, misdiagnosed, and mistreated conditions in the field of medicine.

The term 'bipolar' refers to the two extreme poles of this disorder. The upper pole represents mania, characterized by racing thoughts, often severe insomnia, rapid and pressured speech, paranoia, irrational thinking and behavior, and engaging in high-risk activities with poor insight and judgment. Hypomania, on the other hand, is a milder form of mania, featuring rapid thinking, frequent insomnia, and reduced need for sleep. Hypomanic individuals lack the paranoia and irrationality seen in full-blown mania and can often maintain high functionality. However, the problem is these elevated moods are temporary and can crash into deep and dark depression.

It's worth noting that the majority of individuals with bipolar disorder primarily experience depression rather than mania or hypomania. In fact, many individuals only experience depressive episodes with no manic or hypomanic episodes. This is a critical point because it often leads to missed diagnoses, as providers may focus on detecting mania or hypomania while overlooking bipolar depression.

In brief, bipolar disorder can be classified into three main categories: bipolar 1 disorder (constituting approximately 10% of bipolar cases), bipolar 2 disorder (about 20%), and bipolar NOS (not otherwise specified), which I refer to as Bipolar Spectrum Disorder (comprising about 70%). Bipolar Spectrum Disorder includes cases of bipolar depression within its diagnosis.

FURTHER READING:

If you're interested in reading more details about this topic, check out chapter 11, "The Ups and Downs of Bipolar Disorder," in my first book.

Rachel

At 18 years old, Rachel was referred to me by her primary care doctor and psychologist. She'd been through the psychiatric system for a long time. They wanted to see if I had any new ideas about how to get her stable. After being given cocaine at a party and abusing it, Rachel was hospitalized for a severe manic episode. She became highly manic, irrational, paranoid, and emotional. During the party she drank heavily and caused a scene. Police were called. After evaluating her, they took her to the closest hospital with a psychiatric unit. She remained there for three days.

Her mother went with her to my office the following week. I find it helpful when a parent or a significant other provides a unique perspective than the patient would be able to give.

In contrast, sometimes it is best to see a patient alone on the first visit to gain other useful information without any added stress. Sometimes, doing so leads to some heated disagreements, but what I observe can be extremely helpful in figuring out a situation.

Rachel's recent hospitalization was her third since she was 13. She grew up with a lot of turmoil. Her father was a drug addict, was often absent, or in jail. When he was around, he could be verbally and physically abusive, especially when he drank and used drugs.

She saw her mother being struck on more than one occasion, which created fear and anger toward her father. She was glad when her father left and hoped she'd never see him again.

Her mother shared, "Rachel had episodes of anger and irritability as a child, lashing out. She initially went into the hospital after her first suicide attempt. She took several of my tranquilizers right in front of me." The hospital watched her overnight after her stomach was pumped. She was sent to the pediatric unit for a week.

They sent her home with an SSRI, but she had a bad reaction and felt suicidal. They stopped the medicine and never followed up with the psychiatrist. Instead, they went back to their pediatrician. Since she was not actively suicidal, the doctor decided no further treatment was necessary beyond an analysis by a child psychologist. Rachel went for a brief time but didn't return.

By 16, she'd been cutting her forearms. "It made me feel better for a little while," Rachel told me. "At least I could feel something, and I could hide the marks under my long sleeves."

Rachel dabbled with drugs with other kids. They partied, drank excessively, smoked marijuana, took hallucinogens and tranquilizers like Xanax and Valium. "We only did cocaine once because it's so expensive," she said.

Rachel went on with her story. "When my first boyfriend Neil broke up with me, I felt suicidal. My friends found me at a party passed out in a bedroom after taking several Xanax. I chased it with vodka and orange juice. They called 911 and I went to the ER. They checked me out and sent me to the same psychiatric unit I had just gotten out of. No fun."

Her report said the staff diagnosed her for the second time with major depressive disorder (MDD) and generalized anxiety disorder (GAD). They discharged her with a different antidepressant within the same class as the earlier one. I wasn't surprised she ended up having a bad reaction, just as she had to the first. She took herself off it and told her mother, "I don't want to see that doctor ever again. I don't trust him."

Her pediatrician agreed, voting against another antidepressant. He referred her to a psychologist. She attended until the psychologist brought up things Rachel wasn't comfortable talking about.

At 17, she experienced a third significant incident. She was in a relationship for six months where she'd party a lot with a young man and his friends.

Certain drugs perked her up, gave her energy, and made her feel happy. Others helped her relax and wind down. Her old friends disapproved of his friends and were concerned he was a bad influence. When she discovered a history of him cheating on her, she broke up with him. That sent her spiraling into a deep depression. She confided in friends she was suicidal. "I just didn't want to be around anymore," she admitted. "I checked myself back into the hospital only because Susan said she was going to call the cops on me right there if I didn't. But I told them I wasn't suicidal and promised I would try anything, so they released me."

Her most recent hospitalization was a low point. "I was at a big birthday party and used a lot of cocaine, on top of really slamming the spiked punch down. We found out later they'd put methamphetamines in the mix. I was pissed and started screaming at people. I felt manic and paranoid. When my friends calmed me down, I told them I wanted to die and go to heaven because life is hell on earth," she said. "This time, they were the ones who called 911. It was back to the psych hospital for me."

Her hospital records show Rachel was put on a pair of potent mood stabilizers. To their credit, she wasn't prescribed an antidepressant.

While sedated, her hunger worried her she'd gain weight if she stayed on the medications.

As an aside, in my experience I have found that patients are put on such heavy doses of strong mood stabilizers while in the hospital so that they do not cause problems for the staff. This keeps patients under control. The problem is when outpatient doctors see them, we must deal with the side effects and the hesitancy they have about trying something else due to their previous bad experiences. Hospitals typically think more short-term since they want the condition to be controlled and want them to be discharged as soon as possible.

However, we outpatient doctors need to think more long-term regarding medications that the patient will want to be on and stay on. I saw they still considered MDD and GAD to be the primary diagnoses and felt bipolar disorder was a possibility. What was confusing was that her mania was brought on by heavy amphetamine use, which can trigger mania and paranoia.

When I saw her for the first time, I not only went over the hospital records and all previous records given to me, but also reviewed the new patient form she filled out online. I learned she was more likely getting manic when she did drugs but there were hints of mania and hypomania at other times, though depression seemed to be more predominant in her case. Her family history was obvious. Her father and other relatives on his side and many on her mother's side had all suffered depression and anxiety. It was quite common throughout the entire family.

We discussed her difficulty with sustaining steady relationships with her friends, likely because of her erratic moods and instability. When she saw me, it was about a year into the pandemic, and she had not been able to hold down a steady job, whether part time in high school or after she graduated. She'd suffered through her last couple of years of high school with virtual learning from home. As was the case with many, she didn't learn much at all during that time. She lives in California, which is why she was subjected to distance-learning for so long, and why she was easily able to collect unemployment after graduation.

She was living with her mother and had all her expenses and needs taken care of. Her friends informed her there were a lot of job opportunities available, and the pay was quite good, but she didn't understand why they wanted to work and not just accept free money that required no effort. Her mother would occasionally bring up the benefits of actually working but didn't like facing the anger that accompanied the conversation, so she avoided the subject.

I knew she'd be hesitant about medications given her previous experiences, so I took my time explaining to Rachel and her mother why the previous medications weren't the right ones for her and also why I felt I'd find ones she'd tolerate and would be effective.

After a thorough review of her history, I explained she seemed to have episodes of mania on occasion without drug use but more often with drug use, which hinted towards bipolar one disorder. Much of the time depression was what mostly affected her. She had a mixed bag of the distinct types of bipolar disorder, so she was best described as having bipolar spectrum disorder.

Rachel did not like to hear that diagnosis but understood it when I explained what it meant. She agreed that what I was describing certainly sounded like her. I told them, "I suspect that dopamine is the primary chemical that's imbalanced with GABA, or Gamma Aminobutyric Acid, playing a secondary role. The SSRIs you'd been given before focused on the wrong chemical, which is why they made you feel worse. The mood stabilizers you're on are a bit heavy-handed for you. I will try to avoid any of the problems that you had with previous medications."

"That sounds amazing," she said. "And it all makes total sense now that you've explained everything."

Two of the main problems with mood stabilizers that we try to avoid are their being overly sedative and causing weight gain. I said, "Classic mood stabilizers Lithium and Depakote, which may be taken alone or combined, can be effective and I prescribe them on occasion, but they are often not my first choice due to most people's low tolerance of them. My first-line choice is typically the atypical antipsychotic class."

"What are those?" she asked.

"Most people think they're only used for psychosis and schizophrenia, but they are more often used for the more common diagnosis of bipolar disorder. There are often psychotic features to bipolar disorder, but I assure you, as I have many others, I do not think that you or they are 'crazy' or 'psycho' in the way most people stigmatize others." Clarifying the definition can be reassuring to patients who often feel that they are being ostracized and judged.

With the utmost severe type of bipolar disorder classified as bipolar one disorder, the "classic" mood stabilizers may be combined with an atypical antipsychotic to achieve the best results overall, but it just depends on the individual. We need to make sure side effects do not dissuade the person from staying on the right medications, since compliance can be an issue when it comes to this psychiatric disorder. If they feel significant side effects or alternatively if they feel much better, they may want to stop medications because they think they don't need them anymore.

In Rachel's case I chose Latuda, which is one of the least likely in the atypical antipsychotic class to cause weight gain and sedation. She was hesitant but trusted me after I explained why I really wanted her to try it. I started it at the lowest dose and then 4 days later I had her increase it to the second lowest dose before she checked in with me a week later. I originally figured that this would not be enough, and I found out by our conversation that I was correct, so then I increased the dose two more times until she reached the dose that I figured would be most effective, and thankfully I was correct.

She was sleeping better at night and said that she was able to shut her brain down and get quality sleep. She felt a bit tired the next day, and I expected that that might be the case, so I was already ready to add the second piece that was expected. I added Wellbutrin XL at the lowest dose, which Improved her energy, motivation, and helped to relieve lingering symptoms of depression. Her mother told me, but I could also see myself, that she was smiling more and just seemed overall happier.

The addition of this medication is not for every person with the bipolar diagnosis since in some it may cause agitation and anxiety and may destabilize mood. If this happens, it can be easily stopped. The positive benefits from adding it are not only what I just mentioned but also that it can counteract the fatigue from the mood stabilizer. It can similarly help to counter weight gain in case the mood stabilizer increases one's appetite.

The atypical antipsychotic is called a dopamine antagonist, which slows down and stops dopamine in its tracks when needed. Meanwhile, Wellbutrin XL boosts dopamine during the daytime, leading to the benefits I just mentioned. I refer to this as balancing dopamine 24/7.

At her follow-up visit a month later Rachel was still doing well overall. She admitted she was still having occasional depressive episodes, though not nearly as bad as before, and that she did not feel as good as she had on the previous visit. One of the choices would be trying to increase the Latuda but I felt her dose was already high enough. The other possibility was to try increasing the Wellbutrin XL dose but given her history I felt that there was a better approach.

She was a bit hesitant when I explained that I wanted to add the third medication, and I reminded her that on our first visit my suspicion was that dopamine was the first chemical to address her issue, while GABA was the second one.

I chose Lamictal, which is a unique medication since it is the only antidepressant that focuses on GABA and glutamate and is also a mood stabilizer at the same time. It is a unique medication that I have prescribed often over many years. I don't usually start with it but rather the other ones I mention since it doesn't do as much by itself as it does when added to other medications. It is the slowest medication that I work with so I warned her that it would probably take at least a few weeks to really see the results but that it would be worth the wait if it worked.

I start it at the lowest dose and then increase it quickly while watching for potential side effects which are rare. By the time I saw her back four weeks later she was already feeling better. I titrated it a bit more to figure out the ideal dosage for her, which we ended up finding out pretty quickly. At this point she said her depression was totally under control, as well as any anxiety, and a few months later she told me that she continued to have no further problems with her mood.

Lamictal often serves as mop up duty and can be the last piece of the puzzle that leads to the long-term stability that we are looking for. This was a homerun, which is always the goal with each patient I see.

There were certainly other medication choices for her, but this combination was chosen for her because of my experience using my protocol and based on the detailed history I had gotten from her and her previous records.

Another medication that was not for her but may have been for someone else who had a similar presentation would have been Topamax, which I have discussed in an earlier case. Sometimes despite the mood stabilizers and antidepressants that we use, weight gain can be an issue. If that is, indeed, the case, then Topamax can be a good solution, not just to counteract side effects but also for potential positive benefits such as reduction of anxiety, somatic symptoms, and reduce cravings for certain foods like sugars, carbs, and alcohol if doing so would continue to be an issue.

In Rachel's case, she was able to stop the drug use. For the most part, she only drank alcohol socially on rare occasions.

I encouraged her to continue counseling, which she did, and stuck with it. When society started opening up more, she was interested in getting a job. She understood she was wasting her time and not getting anywhere staying at home while her friends were out working and meeting people that

52

could advance their lives and careers. She felt she had not done well in school, especially towards the end of high school with the shutdowns, but she was actually also interested in going to a local junior college while she was working in order to try to potentially follow a better career path, which both myself and her psychologist were encouraging her to do.

Comments:

As is the case with many bipolar patients, there were a lot of missed opportunities to diagnose her earlier on and thus treat her correctly. The fact that she had significant problems with her mood at an early age and that she attempted suicide and was hospitalized at the age of 13 is a clue that something more than just depression was going on. That should have been figured out after the mishap with the first antidepressant (and more so after the second time), and there was also no proper follow-up by the psychiatrist, though it is not clear that would have helped since the proper diagnosis was not considered during the hospitalization.

The pediatrician also missed the significant clue that when the mood significantly worsens with a "classic" antidepressant, it's a strong indication that bipolar disorder or another related significant mood disorder is the correct diagnosis.

Her strong family history is also a clue to a deeper problem. Bipolar patients often have what I refer to as a "loaded" family history, which means that the genetic factors were strong on both sides of the family, with the bipolar elements obvious on her father's side but also present on her mother's side. The stronger the genetic factors, especially on all sides of the family, make the bipolar diagnosis more likely. The worsening symptoms during puberty were also a strong indicator, especially in girls.

There was another missed opportunity during the second hospitalization by misdiagnosing her again, thus giving her the wrong treatment a second time. The third hospitalization happened when the bipolar diagnosis was first considered, though they felt it was difficult to tell due to the drug use. This is understandable, but the totality of her history should have been a clue that they needed to start thinking towards the upper pole and not just the lower pole. If they had just gotten a complete longitudinal history, they should have been able to figure out the diagnosis despite the illicit drug use that just fueled the disorder and made it worse.

Unfortunately, she did not have adequate follow-up, so she fell through the cracks again. Even though during the most recent hospitalization they realized there was a bipolar element, the medications given were too heavy-handed, as is often the case when someone is hospitalized for the same reasons.

As an aside, a general "rule" in the field of psychiatry is if a patient has one manic episode, that person is classified as having bipolar 1 disorder from then on. I believe we should look at their history and individual presentation. We need to craft therapy to fit their individual needs regardless of their bipolar disorder type.

One of the biggest reasons doctors, including psychiatrists, miss the bipolar diagnosis is a focus on the mania of bipolar 1 disorder. Mania is only 10% of the diagnosis. They may pick up the hypomania of bipolar 2 disorder, or maybe not. Meanwhile the true diagnosis of severe depression is misdiagnosed as the more common unipolar depression.

We must write comprehensive histories for these patients, which many doctors unfortunately don't do. Without a correct diagnosis, how can we come up with a correct treatment plan? We can't.

In Rachel's case, she was able to stop self-medicating. She turned her life around dramatically. She returned to school, work, and enjoyed healthy relationships with her friends. To her credit, she held off on romance, waiting to find someone who was a healthy match for her.

I agreed. With her father figure causing her so much emotional trauma, bad relationships put her at risk of ending up with a guy like her father.

Such relationships can be seen as inevitable because they don't know any difference. In Rachel's case–and with others like her–when properly treated, repeating the patterns is less likely. They're healthy and whole.

Rachel continues to be followed closely. I'm confident her future is bright and filled with hope.

Mike

Mike is a psychologist, 52 years old, who heard about me from colleagues and some of his patients. He reached out for a second opinion. He'd been seeing a psychiatrist for his long-term depression but couldn't tolerate anything he'd been given.

"I had a stable family growing up with my parents and siblings. I felt depression in junior high and high school but figured it was normal. A few of my friends said they felt similar." Mike performed well in school and college, earned a degree in psychology, and worked through graduate school to become a psychotherapist.

He had periods of deep depression and periods where he felt fine throughout college and graduate school.

Mike wanted to study this subject. Not only did he find it interesting, but he might be able to figure out what was wrong with him and help himself. "That way, I'd learn how to help others along the way."

After his studies, Mike didn't have an answer as to why he went back and forth from being in a depression, only to then have times as if nothing was wrong.

Mike started his own practice and noticed his patient's issues. "They usually had reasons for why they felt depressed, but I didn't think I did. I was ashamed and felt weak, so I just buried my feelings. In my 20s and 30s, though, things got so bad I saw a psychiatrist."

He tried different antidepressants for years, but only Wellbutrin worked, and that was short-term. It made him jittery and nervous, so he'd stop and restart it. "The psychiatrist also practiced psychotherapy, which was helpful. I tried focusing on exercising regularly, eating well, and keeping my weight down. I tried practiced relaxation techniques, which is something I'd taught my patients."

When I took his history, I saw a pattern of cyclical depression: meaning depression lasting for a period before improving. Then the pattern repeats.

Michael sometimes went three months between episodes, sometimes one month, or up to six months or longer. There was just no rhyme or reason. He had no discernible history of mania or hypomania, but his depression went deep and dark, with occasional suicidal thoughts.

Mike didn't want to follow through with the ideation, so it bothered him he even thought it.

He suffered with insomnia, as many bipolar patients do. "When I don't sleep well, I feel tired and terrible the next day." When one is hypomanic, there's a decreased need for sleep. They function fine the next day, often with more than average energy.

Mike showed no signs of high energy, just a severe, unrelenting depression. "I was powerless. I felt guilty I couldn't beat it, despite my chosen career."

Mike's family history was loaded on both sides with mood disorder variants.

The diagnosis was easy since I took a complete longitudinal history and understood why his diagnosis was missed and mistreated for so long. "I believe you have bipolar depression," I told him.

"I have bipolar patients and I don't really resemble them," he argued. He thought for a moment. "But now that you mention it? That makes sense."

"It's hard to see when it's happening to you," I said. "And we both know bipolar comes in many variations and doesn't always present itself the same in any two people."

I knew that dopamine was a factor, as shown by his brief positive response to Wellbutrin XL. That medication led to anxiety.

"How about we try one of the newer dopamine antagonist mood stabilizers? Vraylar might also help your energy since it can be stimulating," I said.

He agreed.

Within the next 1 to 2 weeks, he felt better. "I think my depression is about 50% better. I'd be happy staying at that level because it's already better than my baseline."

"That's wonderful. I hear you," I said, "but we're not done yet. I want to add Lamictal. It's a unique medication, as it's the only antidepressant that modulates GABA and glutamate, while also being a mood stabilizer. It's the slowest medication I work with. It doesn't typically do much the first couple of weeks. By the third or fourth week, it kicks in."

During his four-week follow-up visit, he shared great news. "It's working. You were right. It was worth the wait."

We titrated it to a higher and more optimal dose over the following month.

"Do you remember when you told me you wanted me to feel like my old self?" he asked. "Well, that's not the case."

My stomach tightened.

He grinned. "That's because I've never felt this good my whole life!"

Mike entered a state of complete remission, the goal for every patient. He's remained on these two medications with no further augmentation needed.

We discovered the right combination through rational trial and error. For instance, if Vraylar wasn't tolerated and a sedating mood stabilizer was chosen, or if Vraylar worked well but was sedating, adding Wellbutrin XL could be tolerated and work.

As an aside, I don't like advertising name brand products. I work with many and don't want to play favorites. There were other choices in the same family as Vraylar, such as Rexulti, Abilify, and more. It depends on the experience and comfort of the prescriber and knowing the details of each psychotropic medication. That's vital if you want to achieve the best results.

Mike couldn't believe how much his quality of life had changed. We both marveled at how disastrous the effect of the pandemic of 2020 to 2022 was regarding mental health.

I saw a definite worsening of anxiety, depression, bipolar disorder, PTSD, OCD, and all the other types of mental illness during those disastrous years. He and I were busier than ever during that time. Unfortunately, many couldn't find providers that could help them since many were so busy, which is unfortunate.

Mike and I continue to refer patients to each other to this day and try to help as many people as we can.

Comments:

Bipolar disorder is probably the most misunderstood and mistreated diagnosis in psychiatry. A shocking statistic: it takes 3 to 4 doctors 7 to 10 years to diagnose bipolar disorder. Yes, you heard that right. Can you imagine taking that many doctors that long to diagnose diabetes, heart disease, cancer? Me either. That needs to change. That whole time the patients were misdiagnosed, and the treatments were based on the incorrect diagnosis, which just doesn't work out well.

The real reason so many doctors, primary care, and psychiatrists alike, miss this diagnosis is that they do not take a detailed history throughout that person's life. They also tend not to think about bipolar disorder when the presenting symptom is depression. People come in when they're depressed, not when they're manic or hypomanic and out "having fun." If we don't get a longitudinal history, then we will not pick up on these important clues.

Another clue often missed is depression getting worse and better over time in a cyclical way. That's not typical for unipolar depression, which is more common.

What really gets to me is seeing providers trying so many different antidepressants within the same class. They don't understand they're just beating a dead horse. The definition of insanity is doing the same thing repeatedly and expecting different results. I saw so much insanity that it drew me to this field during my time as a family doctor. I decided I had to do something about it.

Thankfully, after many years, I've used a rational pharmaceutical approach to achieve mind-body health.

Antidepressants can be helpful in some bipolar cases, including SSRIs and SNRIs. They're often needed to achieve full remission, especially in cases of bipolar spectrum disorder, such as bipolar depression, and sometimes with bipolar 1 and bipolar 2 disorder. It's least likely with bipolar 1 disorder since the focus is on mood stabilizers. Antidepressants can be a principal factor as long as they don't destabilize the patient's mood.

I have learned how to get quick and safe results by choosing the right psychotropic medication to begin with. This develops a good foundation. It's important to choose augmentation strategies until the patient is in complete remission, meaning completely well in mind, body, and spirit.

It is extremely important to understand the *off-label* benefits of medications. Being familiar with the benefits leads to the most innovative treatments.

I love treating these patients because I enjoy the dramatic results and changed, restored lives.

CHAPTER 4

ADD/ADHD:
Attention Deficit Disorder/Attention
Deficit Hyperactivity Disorder

ADD/ADHD's onset is usually in early childhood, but it often worsens with age. This disorder breaks down into three presentations: Inattentive, Impulsive, and Hyperactive. A patient can also have a combination of these.

The inattentive spaces out, doodles, and stares out the window, hearing little of what the teacher is saying.

The impulsive does things without thinking about the consequences and gets into trouble.

The hyperactive gets the most attention because they're up and down and tend to get into other's business.

Early signs are evident in children, especially hyperactivity. Symptoms present more as the child enters kindergarten and 1st and 2nd grade. Once diagnosed, the earlier treatment starts the better. Doing so positively alters the course of a child's life.

Treating kids with ADD medications is controversial. It shouldn't be. Many parents are resistant to the thought of "drugging" their kids. I work to convince them if I feel it's in the child's best interest. There are other behavioral interventions, but it's a medical problem with a medical solution.

ADD has nothing to do with intelligence but everything to do with the ability to focus, concentrate, staying on task, being organized, and on their game.

Early treatment saves years of grief and makes school and life much easier. Some kids are ashamed of earning bad grades and are chastised for incomplete, late, or missing schoolwork.

Some internalize this, affecting their self-esteem. Ignoring treatment increases the likelihood of drug abuse, especially during the teen years.

When prescribing stimulants, some say, "You might as well put them on meth. It's the same thing." That's completely ridiculous, but some won't be convinced of the truth.

If not treated properly, people are more likely to self-medicate and fail to achieve their true potential.

The stories from actual patients that follow demonstrate how ADD/ADHD can present in a wide variety of ways.

FURTHER READING:

If you would like to read more about this topic, go to chapter 10 of my first book or listen to my four-part podcast series on the subject.

Ryan

"I always struggled in high school," Ryan confided in me ten years later when he was 28. "I couldn't concentrate when the teacher talked or when it was time to do my homework."

His parents did most of the homework for him since they wanted him to pass. "They tried to push me, but it was hard. My teacher brought up the possibility I had ADD and wanted me to get help. My parents didn't believe in medications for kids and knew about other natural and homeopathic methods. We tried different diets and supplements, but they didn't make much of a difference."

The teacher placed him up front, gave him more time to complete tests, and allowed testing in a quieter area or in a different room. "It helped a little, but not significantly," he shared. The pattern continued from grade school through middle school but was at its worst during high school.

"My grades were so bad I barely graduated by pushing through the public school system. I took GED exam and barely passed," he said. "I tried going to a local junior college for a semester but dropped out when I realized I didn't want to continue with school. I felt like a failure."

He found a job at the front desk of a large office screening calls.

That's when he found me, a decade out of high school.

Ryan was a nice, friendly guy. His boss and coworkers loved him. Since he knew the job so well, they kept him on. Meanwhile, others who started after him moved up the ranks or on to better jobs. Ryan was comfortable where he was.

His friend was one of my patients I'd treated successfully for ADD and she referred him to me.

His diagnosis was clear when I took his history. He had inattentive ADD since an early age. Drawing two neurons connecting, I explained how communication between cells occurs and how ADD medications resolve imbalances by forcing the neurochemicals to connect properly. They don't do so on their own; the main reason being genetic predisposition, which a person can't control.

Ryan agreed to try a stimulant, the most common and effective treatment. Over the following year he was promoted twice. His employers considered him for another position, but he chose to return to school full-time. "Now that I realized I could focus, concentrate, and stay on task, I wanted to give school another shot and go after a business degree."

He talked to his friends and family about his choices. His parents came with him on the next visit. I thought I'd get chastised for "drugging" their child but received the opposite reaction. They couldn't believe the difference in their son, and shared they felt guilty he wasn't treated back when the teachers and doctor first urged them to.

Instead, they listened to their friends and did internet research, which often leads to misinformation. "We feel guilty we held him back and didn't realize his potential and thought his grades reflected his true intelligence," his mother admitted.

"It wasn't you," I told them. "From our first session, it was obvious Ryan was quite intelligent. His diagnosis, which he inherited from his dad's side, wasn't his fault. You believed you were doing what was best for your son. We can't go back. It's time to just look ahead."

"Very true," his mom said.

"He's young and has plenty of time to go to school and improve his career," I said. "There's no reason for guilt and shame when it comes to conditions beyond a person's control."

I was happy. "I've been in my first successful relationship that's lasted more than a few months," he said. "Pretty sure she's the one."

To me? Ryan's outcome was wonderful and one of the main reasons I keep persevering. The Corona Protocol works.

Quinn

Quinn's first appointments with me began when she was in high school. She excelled in grade school but struggled during eighth grade. I diagnosed her with ADD, which surprised her and her parents because she'd done well academically.

"ADD has nothing to do with intelligence and everything to do with being able to focus," I told them.

Soon after treatment, Quinn did much better in school, even graduating with a 4.0 GPA. She was the type of student who hardly got an A-. She was distraught the one time she earned a B+ and vowed it'd never happen again.

I was thrilled to hear she'd been accepted into her first-choice college—my alma mater—the University of Southern California, majoring in biology and Pre-Med, just as I had. I didn't see her again until her junior year. I figured she must've seen a doctor on campus to fill her prescriptions.

"You're not far away and you can come into the office or have a virtual appointment if you need your prescriptions," I said.

"Well, I stopped taking those," Quinn admitted. "I don't think I need them. I'm doing fine through my own hard work and discipline. I don't want to be weak and be medicated and dependent on a pill."

I was shocked but pressed for more details. "How's college going for you?"

"Things haven't been going to plan. I've spent most of my time studying in my room or the library. I haven't made a lot of friends. I don't go out a lot. And it's not like my grades are awesome. I don't get it."

"How has it been working through the pandemic?" I asked.

"Very isolated and lonely. I'm a junior and the classes are harder than ever."

I said, "The last two years of college are the hardest. It's crucial you get treated right away to get through it."

"But that would mean I failed."

"I understand you feel that way but it's not true. You're just facing your diagnosis and treating it. You don't want to jeopardize getting into medical school. From someone who's been there, it's much harder and you'll need to be at the top of your game."

"I hear you," Quinn said. "Let's take care of it."

Within a few weeks, Quinn got back on track and earned her usual A grades again.

"Medical schools are going to be impressed you hit those marks during the hardest years," I said. "You made the right choice."

"Thank you," Quinn said. "I'm grateful for your help. I just wish I hadn't been so reclusive."

"You'll catch up."

She did, sending me reports of how she found time to date, have friends, and enjoyed seeing many USC football games as they beat their opponents. She kept her GPA up and got into medical school.

Comments:

Ryan and Quinn's ADD presented differently but were both intelligent in their own ways. Quinn's IQ helped achieve her goal of becoming a physician. Ryan's potential was always present but untapped. It was exhilarating watching their transformations prove why a diagnosis must be made and treated right away. As with bipolar disorder, ADD is also a significantly underdiagnosed, undertreated, misdiagnosed, and mistreated condition.

This story illustrated a key point. Many mood disorders, such as anxiety disorders, depressive disorders, bipolar disorders, and others, can coexist with ADD. To treat patients with multiple disorders, combining stimulants with antidepressants and/or mood stabilizers can create a cocktail that treats them quite well all at once.

Here's one last case story I can't resist sharing.

Eric

Eric was 24 when he first met with me. He showed symptoms of two types of anxiety: primarily social with some secondary general. He responded well to treatment, showing improvement within the first couple weeks.

During those sessions, I discovered another layer. "You have ADD," said.

"Wow. Are you sure? On top of the anxiety?" Eric asked.

"Yes. I've seen all the signs."

Eric often interrupted me and didn't always comprehend what I said. As an exercise, I had him try to write down what I said but he kept getting distracted and losing focus.

When patients have a mood disorder and ADD, I treat the mood issues, such as anxiety, depression, bipolar disorder, or others, first. ADD gets treated after. Sometimes, it's already improved from treating the mood.

"In some cases, treatment of the mood disorder can resolve the ADD symptoms, thus not needing a stimulant," I said. "Often, adding a stimulant leads to more thorough results."

"Makes sense to me. I want to be able to focus better on reading. It'll help my paperwork, and with returning emails faster."

The added stimulant helped his anxiety, too.

It seems counterintuitive, but when one has ADD, a stimulant has a calming effect on the brain and reduces anxiety.

"My boss is thrilled at my work and gave me a raise if I keep this up," Eric said.

Thrilled, he continued our visits. Soon, he was dating. "Once society opened up, I met someone. We've been together three months, which is the longest I've ever been with someone. I get what my other girlfriends told me now. It was like I was only half-listening. Now, I can look her in the eyes. I don't interrupt her."

"That's great," I said.

"Doc, I finally get it. I think I've found the secret of a successful relationship. Chicks just want you to listen to them."

I laughed. "Women talk about twice as much as men. After being married more than 30 years, I agree with your conclusion. Communication is the key to a successful relationship, you figured out on your own what it takes many of us much longer, if at all, to understand."

PART TWO

The Really Tough Cases

Let's highlight some difficult patients. I've seen my share of tough cases of anxiety disorders, depression, bipolar disorder, and ADD/ADHD. Even though some cases are easier to resolve, and some are more perplexing, I love the challenge. I enjoy figuring out intricate puzzles, and the human being is the living puzzle I most enjoy solving. It is exciting to see people who have long struggled quickly getting their lives back.

Many patients arrive in a desperate state. Some don't want to live any longer if it means living the same way. Many have seen several doctors without getting to the root causes of their problems. I want to be the one who finds answers and gets them on track. I want them to thrive, not just survive. When I see their excitement, I'm elated. It's humbling when they share how much their lives have improved and have discovered true happiness and joy.

CHAPTER 5

PTSD

PTSD is a mental health condition triggered by experiencing or witnessing a terrifying event. Many have heard of it as something soldiers from war go through. I've had the pleasure of working with many veterans, evaluating and treating them for PTSD. I have profound respect for those who've risked their lives to preserve the moral ideals and values the United States represents. I'm sure to thank each of them for their sacrifice and service.

There are other examples of traumas and terrors leading to PTSD, such as victims of violent crimes such as armed robbery, rape, domestic emotional and physical abuse, through natural disasters, and other life-threatening scenarios.

PTSD leaves impactful, long-term damage. Thankfully, treatments exist to help them to move on and thrive.

Bruce

After spending many years in the VA system, Bruce was referred to me by another veteran. A Marine who'd served in Vietnam in the 1960s and 1970s, Bruce spent time near the front lines in active combat. After reviewing his intake form and VA hospital records, I was struck by his considerable amount of trauma.

Bruce had difficulty talking about the war. He got choked up. "I'm sorry," he said. "It's still so present in my mind."

"You have absolutely nothing to apologize for," I said. "I need to know every detail about what traumatized you."

"When I was at the base, a supposedly safe space, we were attacked by rockets and mortars day and night. We slept with our boots on and our guns by our side. When the guard yelled 'Incoming' we'd drop to the floor to try and find some shelter. You can't ever relax because you're in constant fear of dying."

I kept listening.

"I saw many of my fellow soldiers dying or severely wounded. I saw a couple of people blown up when they couldn't avoid an incoming rocket and the horrible aftermath. I'll never forget one soldier who was obviously dying, pleading with me to help, but there was nothing I or anyone could do."

"That's a lot to carry," I told him.

"I killed several of our enemy. I'm not sure how many and I don't want to know. I get that they were the enemy, and I was just doing my job, but I can't stop thinking about them having families that'd never see them again. As much as I wish they weren't, those thoughts haunt me every day."

He had several classic symptoms of PTSD. Before the war, he never had any mental health issues. That changed since coming back home. He was bitter at the response from some Americans, who called them names such as baby killers and other vile things.

Bruce suffered insomnia. "I sometimes don't want to sleep because I have vivid nightmares … flashbacks of what I went through. I wake up screaming. I don't recognize my wife at first."

His dreams haunted him, causing a lack of sleep, leading to fatigue, lack of focus and concentration, and reducing his motivation and drive.

Amy, his wife, chimed in. "I'm concerned about his reduced memory, especially for recent events. He gets angry and irritable. Bruce isn't like the man I knew before the war."

Bruce obviously showed symptoms of anxiety and depression.

"He's become more withdrawn and doesn't participate in things he enjoyed before," Amy said. "Bruce startles easily and hates loud noises. He doesn't like depictions of wars on TV, movies, or books. He hates the Fourth of July, same as our dogs."

"I'm surprised your PTSD hasn't been adequately diagnosed and treated" I said to Bruce. "You've been to some individual and group therapy, but the medical treatment was woefully inadequate." To be fair, he was offered medical help but refused it. "I know there's a stigma for vets. That soldier mentality of not complaining and being tough—don't show signs of weakness. It's counter to a soldier's machismo image."

"I don't understand why my life was spared while so many others died. Part of me wishes I would have died there, too," Bruce confided.

"That's heartbreaking to hear," I said. "You're experiencing survivor's guilt." It's hard to imagine what he went through, and the aftermath years later. "But that isn't a weakness. It's not your fault."

I drew him a diagram of two neurons connecting. "The trauma you experienced threw off the balance of the chemicals in your nervous system. They haven't rebalanced since and can't without medical help. I suggest trying psychotherapy. There's a specialized type called EMDR, which is well known to help with all kinds of trauma including PTSD."

Bruce said, "I'm listening."

"It's a difficult therapy. Patients can relive difficult experiences, but it's well worth it. The results work. The idea is not burying painful memories while learning to deal with them. Only then can you move on."

My first task was balancing his nervous system. He deserved nothing less. Initially reluctant to accept my advice about starting a psychotropic medication, he soon agreed to follow through.

His first intervention was an SNRI.

During our next visit, Bruce was smiling. "I'm feeling so much better. My anxiety has gone way down. I'm not as jumpy. I'm sleeping better and it's easier to focus."

"It's a thrill hearing you report such great results," I said. "That's what I hope for. You've suffered far too long."

"Thanks, doc. Overall, I feel better emotionally and physically but there's still some fatigue and lack of motivation. My memory's not back to normal. There's less nightmares but they're still not completely gone."

"Seeing you respond to medicine so well, let's add Wellbutrin XL and Prazosin. Prazosin is a blood pressure medication, but it can help to resolve nightmares associated with trauma such as PTSD."

Two weeks later, he came in with Amy. "I can't thank you enough for giving me my husband back. I knew him before he went to Vietnam, and we got married after he returned home." She squeezed his hand. They looked like young kids in love again. "Bruce hasn't felt this well for over 50 years. His energy and motivation are way better."

"That's thanks to the Wellbutrin XL," I said.

"My focus, concentration and memory have gotten good enough that I want to get together with my friends to play cards and go golfing. Also, the Prazosin at bedtime seems to have taken away the nightmares. My dreams are now peaceful," Bruce said.

At his one-month and three-month checkups, Bruce continued to live the life he deserved.

Some of the most satisfying results come from patients suffering from PTSD. The stories of veterans and others suffering traumatic events affecting the nervous system are heart-wrenching and have, at times, brought me to tears.

They don't deserve what's happened. Thankfully, treatment allows them to return to normal quickly. Results can last the rest of their lives when appropriately treated with the amazing array of readily available psychotropic medications.

CHAPTER 6

Eating Disorders

Abnormal or disturbed eating habits characterize eating disorders. It's a complex mental health condition requiring psychological and medical attention. Consisting of many elements including psychological, medical, hormonal, and mental/psychiatric components, they're often present in those with a history of severe trauma, such as PTSD.

Common in Westernized countries, who are preoccupied with thinness and body shape, they're not as significant an issue in other countries.

There are many distinct types of eating disorders. We'll describe the three most common and well-known throughout this section.

FURTHER READING:

A more comprehensive discussion appears in Chapter 12: "Eaten Alive by Eating Disorders" in volume one of my *Healing the Mind and Body: The Trilogy.*

Anorexia Nervosa

This condition generally develops during adolescence and young adulthood and tends to affect women more than men. They perceive themselves as overweight, even if they're dangerously underweight. They are obsessive about watching their weight, counting calories, and knowing the fat content of each food they consider eating. Their self-esteem revolves around their weight and body shape. They have a distorted body image and deny being seriously underweight. I think of eating disorders as an obsessive-compulsive behavior like OCD, but the obsessions revolve around food, especially about the lack thereof for anorexics.

Anorexia nervosa can be damaging to the body, especially the brain. They can experience bone thinning like osteoporosis. Hair and nails go brittle. Menstrual cycles become irregular and can lack menses. Anorexia can lead to infertility, electrolyte abnormalities, and death.

Bulimia Nervosa

Like anorexia nervosa, which also tends to develop during adolescence and early adulthood, bulimia nervosa is more common in women. Both conditions also are common in certain sports, such as gymnastics, dancing, and wrestling for boys. It tends to affect athletes who focus on weight. People with bulimia often eat unusually copious amounts of food over a specific period of time, progressing until the person is painfully full.

On the flip side, there are others who purge lesser amounts of food. They cannot stop eating or control the quantity. This is the obsessive-compulsive behavior bulimics have difficulty controlling.

Common purging behaviors include forced vomiting, laxatives, diuretics, enemas, and excessive exercise. As opposed to binge eating disorder, they tend to maintain a relatively normal weight. Their self-esteem is overly influenced by their body shape. They have an intense fear of gaining weight. Symptoms include an inflamed, sore throat, swollen salivary glands, worn tooth enamel, tooth decay, acid reflux, abdominal irritation, dehydration, and hormonal disturbances. In severe cases, they can also develop electrolyte abnormalities concerning sodium, potassium, and calcium. This can lead to serious cardiac issues, which are sometimes fatal.

Binge Eating Disorder

Binge eating is one of the most common eating disorders. Binge eaters characteristically eat unusually copious amounts of generally unhealthy foods over short periods. The feelings are uncontrollable—the key element of their obsessive-compulsive behavior. They don't restrict calories and don't engage in purging behaviors, such as vomiting, excessive exercise, or the others. Often done secretly, until they're uncomfortably full, binge eaters do so despite not feeling hungry.

They often feel distress, shame, disgust, or guilt, when thinking about their binge eating behavior. They tend to be overweight, with some morbidly obese. They may have medical complications such as type 2 diabetes, hypertension, heart disease, and increased stroke risk.

Jennifer

Jennifer's psychologist referred her when she was 25 years old. She was the third therapist Jennifer had seen, along with a handful of medical doctors, all seeking answers.

She filled three pages of details in her patient intake form. The average is two.

From the form, I diagnosed her with a severe eating disorder along with other related, coexisting diagnoses.

My process is to block out an hour for a new patient. I could have used more for Jennifer; there was a lot to address.

While getting a patient's history, I allow the patient to talk as long as possible without interruption. This provides time to share all the information they consider important. It's the most vital information to hear in order to figure out how to best help.

It's essential to pay attention to all the numerous details and clues. After establishing their baseline, I ask them to start at the beginning. "Tell me about your childhood, adolescence, and adulthood. Start back when you felt your best. How would you like to feel again, if possible?"

"I'm not sure," Jennifer said, lost. "I can't remember a time I wasn't stress-free. I've had anxiety since I was a kid. I was shy, except around my parents and close family members. I had bad separation anxiety when my mother dropped me off at school. I'd cry for quite a while after she left. I'd wear myself out and stop." She shook her head. "I had a few friends growing up but liked being alone. Other people made me anxious."

She continued and I listened. "One thing I loved was eating, which calmed my nerves. My small group of friends discovered endless types of junk food we loved. That being said? I still preferred being alone so no one could see what I was doing. My parents were concerned by middle school. Going into high school, I became overweight. I got teased a lot. Kids in high school were brutal."

Jennifer was open to change. "My parents were concerned and sent me to a nutritionist to teach me proper eating habits. After hearing what the nutritionist said, I paid attention to the details of the food I ate. I was horrified by what I saw and read online. My eating habits completely violated every dietary rule. I learned what foods contained fat, what the different carbohydrates were, and how sugars affect the metabolism. I counted calories and watched fat content. I lost the weight I originally wanted, but it wasn't enough."

Her parents enrolled her in gymnastics for her to exercise regularly and teach discipline. "I liked it but spent most of my time comparing my body to the other gymnasts. The other girls were thinner. I had to change that, so I restricted more until I was so weak, I couldn't compete."

Jennifer returned to her nutritionist who told her she was taking things too far and she needed a more balanced diet. "I didn't like hearing that because all I heard was how much weight I'd gain if I followed her recommendations." She did not want to stay in gymnastics because she didn't like believing she didn't look as good as the other girls. Her parents relented, knowing gymnastics wasn't for her.

No matter what they did for her, Jennifer wasn't satisfied. They demanded she needed to find some type of exercise to replace gymnastics. She exercised solo by power walking and jogging but didn't increase her dietary needs accordingly.

By high school, she was tired of working so hard and still not being happy. Jennifer decided to break her dietary habits and go back to comfort eating. She gained weight, which upset her mother. "I felt my daughter was moving backward," her mother said.

Her older brother and father teased her. Her father pinched her on the side and told her she needed to, "Do something about this."

Her mother took a banana out of her hand she was going to peel and eat because the outside was brown, which meant it had too much sugar.

"A girl in high school told me about purging. I could eat whatever I wanted and get rid of it in secret," Jennifer said.

Because she didn't lose enough weight by purging, she took long walks or jogged for 2 to 3 hours. She used laxatives when she was too full or constipated. Her friends and family saw her as being more withdrawn. She hid her anxiety attacks and learned how to eat and exercise for relief.

While she hid her binging and purging, she found cutting her forearms made her feel better, too. She hid the gouges by wearing long-sleeved blouses and sweaters. She avoided people.

Her mother took her back to the nutritionist who confirmed Jennifer seemed to have transitioned from an anorexic to a bulimic condition. Her glands swelled and she showed symptoms of acid reflux, along with abdominal pain and bloating.

Her dentist noticed her teeth and gums showed signs of overexposure to stomach acid. She required extensive dental work to fix the damage.

Her friends were talking behind her back, so she avoided them. She was grateful to graduate and go off to college, Jennifer left her friends and former life behind. She majored in psychology, believing she'd discover some truths about herself.

She didn't get much exercise, since she spent a lot of time in her room studying and eating, getting rid of it when she ate too much. With only one roommate her first two years, she hid her habits. Junior and senior years were easier as she had her own room: her safe space.

Over time, she learned how much to eat to maintain a weight that wasn't as thin as she'd have hoped but was comfortable with. She was lonely and sad but didn't trust others who might discover her secrets.

"I didn't let anyone get close. I had some short-term boyfriends, but I was ashamed. I thought I was fat. I was tired all the time and had zero motivation. I stopped exercising and just watched TV or did my schoolwork. I was most comfortable when I was alone."

Jennifer began treatment with me during her third year of graduate school, getting a Ph.D. to become a psychotherapist. She was aware she had a mixed eating disorder.

Remarks and teasing from those closest to her contributed to the underlying factors leading up to her eating disorder. As her mother also struggled with weight, there was also a genetic factor.

"These get worse from middle school to high school since this is when puberty occurs. It's also when kids tease," I said. "What can start as a jest can sometimes lead to bullying. Neurochemicals can start going out of balance at that age, contributing to obsessive thinking, fluctuating moods, and body feelings."

"You're spot on," she said.

"Any stressors you think may be contributing to your condition?"

Jennifer said, "Grad school is challenging, and I was in a healthy relationship, but I'm not feeling stable enough for that to be possible now."

She'd purge daily, less than she used to. She used strong mouthwash mixed with hydrogen peroxide to prevent damaging her teeth. "I'd wait until night to binge sugars and carbohydrates. I couldn't help the cravings. I was out of control and felt guilty and ashamed."

To regain control, she saw a new psychologist and made some progress. The doctor offered medical treatment. Jennifer tried a couple of medications: an SSRI and Wellbutrin XL, though not together. She didn't like how antidepressants felt. The SSRI made her tired, and the Wellbutrin made her anxious, so she stopped them.

"I'm nervous to take another medication after that," she said.

"The only way to fix this problem for good is by addressing the underlying problem and treating it in a supportive and curative way."

She seemed intrigued. I drew a diagram of two neurons connecting. "I suspect you have three imbalances: serotonin, dopamine, and GABA. Psychotropic medications work by attaching to the nerve cells and redirecting traffic, which forces the chemicals to move in the right direction. This results in a re-creation, for the first time in years, a feeling of normality and feeling of self, with true inner happiness and joy."

I started her on a low dose of the SSRI Prozac and titrated slowly to a higher range. Why did I not choose an SNRI, my usual first choice? Because I didn't suspect that norepinephrine was a key factor. With eating disorders serotonin is usually a significant factor. Patients with anorexia nervosa usually require a low dose, while people with bulimia nervosa typically need a dose in the higher range of normal. The medicine would help her obsessive thinking and calm her anxiety.

She'd feel tired and apathetic, but it'd be temporary and would signal it'd be time to add the second medication. A few weeks later I added Wellbutrin XL to boost dopamine. I checked a full lab panel to ensure her electrolytes were normal and she was stable for treatment. Adding the Wellbutrin XL boosted her energy and motivation and resolved her depression. When adding it to the SSRI, it didn't cause anxiety like it had on its own. Wellbutrin is usually better as an add-on agent rather than a first treatment.

Adding Topamax in the early evening balanced her GABA. Titrating it over four weeks to the optimal dose resolved her cravings for sugars and carbohydrates, stopping her from binging and purging. It helped her anxiety, headaches, and neck, shoulder and upper back pain. "My whole body just feels better."

Jennifer was all smiles during her third visit, she showed off her beautiful white teeth. It was exciting to see her transformation. "I'm not obsessing over food and I'm actually eating a proper well-balanced diet throughout the day."

She looked healthy and full of energy and motivation back. She exercised regularly and reasonably.

"Psychotropic medications don't control a person—they help a person be in control. You couldn't help what you went through since eating disorders are so persistent and difficult to resolve. There are so many factors at play, with genetics, upbringing, hormonal changes, and situational stressors all out of one's control."

A few months later, she had another surprise. "I'm in my first really healthy relationship that's lasted more than a month or two. I shared my story with Brad. I was both surprised and relieved when he accepted me for who I am and didn't judge me for my past. He thanked me for telling him, since he wanted to know everything about me."

Graduate school was doing much better since she had more drive and determination to put the work in and get better grades.

"I made peace with my family," she said. "I understand where they were coming from. They couldn't help certain things, either. By the way? I referred my mom to you after telling her how much you helped me."

During her mom's first appointment, she asked, "Can you help me like you helped my daughter?"

"Of course. I'd be honored to," I told her.

She's doing well now, too. The Corona Protocol works.

CHAPTER 7
Schizophrenia

Schizophrenia is a serious mental disorder in which reality is interpreted abnormally. It may present through combinations of hallucinations, delusions, and extremely disorganized thinking and behavior, impairing daily functioning. Some with schizophrenia are high functioning, while others can be completely disabled. This chronic diagnosis needs long-term treatment, which can dramatically improve the condition and improve their long-term outlook.

Delusions are false beliefs not based in reality. Some feel they're being followed, or harassed, and are suspicious of others. They may misread gestures and comments, taking them personally. Hallucinations involve seeing or hearing things that don't exist. They believe they're real. Hallucinations can happen through any of the senses; hearing voices is the most common and classic type.

Disorganized thinking displays as disorganized speech. They may not answer questions directly and put together words that don't make sense to anybody except themselves. This is referred to as a word salad.

Disorganized and abnormal motor behaviors include unpredictable agitation, along with childlike silliness. Their behaviors aren't goal oriented. Their body movements may be inappropriate, bizarre and display excessive movement.

The symptoms thus far are referred to as positive symptoms. Negative symptoms refer to basic functioning, such as neglecting personal hygiene. They may appear to lack emotion and may avoid eye contact. They tend to freeze their facial expressions and speak in a monotone. They may lose interest in everyday activities, become socially withdrawn, and lack the ability to experience pleasure.

There may be periods when they do better, while at other times they're worse. In men, Schizophrenia typically starts in the early to mid-20s, though it can start in the teens.

In women, it typically starts in the latter 20s. It's rare to first see it in children or middle age.

Schizophrenia is a severe diagnosis, but thankfully, we have serious treatments that work extremely well.

Brian

Brian was referred to me at 23. He and his parents filled out separate intake forms to explore both their perspectives, which can be enlightening.

During his first visit, it was important to get his perspective about what he felt was going on with him. I then had his parents come in for the second half of the visit to share their perspective about what they felt was going on with their son.

They told me he was shy growing up and kept to himself a lot, but his parents didn't worry about him because he was getting good grades and devoted a lot of time to his studies. He loved working with computers and spent endless hours playing video games alone in his room. His parents tried to encourage him to go out and play and be more active, but he only did the minimal amount and tried to avoid others whenever possible.

He was teased at times, especially going into middle school and high school, since he came across as socially awkward, and since he did so well at school, he had been termed a nerd and a geek. His parents encouraged him to join the science club and math club at the high school, and he checked them out but didn't feel comfortable being around that many other people.

His parents gave up trying to get him involved in activities but were happy that he had such a high GPA and wanted to attend college to get a Computer Engineer degree. At college, he continued to excel academically but spent most of his time in his room or at the library, preferably by himself and far enough away from other people, so they didn't bother him.

He didn't get involved with any of the social opportunities available on campus and spent his off time in his room playing video games for hours. He felt he was living within his game since the beautiful woman with the long dark hair would occasionally speak to him when he was sleeping, even when he was trying to think about something else. It felt so real to him when she'd join him in his dreams on certain evenings. She would also join him while she was inside the game. He could tell that she was interested in him by the way that she looked at him and treated him. He thought he could hear her whispering to him and could occasionally briefly see her in the corner of his vision, but when he looked, she'd disappear.

Occasionally, teachers and other students would see him muttering to himself, and he sometimes seemed unaware of others around him.

He'd graduated from college and continued to live with his parents where he felt safe, so they were able to see firsthand how his behavior had progressed, and they were concerning to them. He spent hours in his room when he was working in his first year out of college as a computer engineer.

Due to the pandemic, he could work full-time from home, so he could therefore easily avoid being around other people, which he was happy about. This resulted in Brian spending most of his time in his room, either working or playing video games. His parents were concerned he didn't seem to shower or brush his teeth often, so they would remind him when they could see or smell that he had not been taking care of himself.

There were also concerns that he seemed to be often talking while he was playing video games as if he was having a conversation with someone else when they knew that there was nobody else in the room with him. When they asked him who he was talking to he told them that there were other people that he played the game with, but they could hear the conversations and that didn't make any sense to them. They knew that he wasn't telling the truth.

Brian could also hear the voices of his neighbors, so he would go out to look and see if he could catch them spying on him. His next-door neighbor's teenage daughter would occasionally lay out in the backyard in her bikini, and he knew that she was attracted to him and that she was trying to tease him. He knew that it was wrong what she was doing, and he was ashamed about how he was thinking about her. It was her fault for tempting him.

He suspected that it was more than just those neighbors, so he kept track, since he knew that he was being spied on and watched. When he told his parents about this, they told him everything was fine and that he was just imagining this, which made him angry that they were dismissing his concerns because he knew that what he was sensing was real.

He started keeping track of the license plates of the cars on the block so he could identify them in case they broke into their home. His parents noticed that he was having conversations with people that weren't there, and the dialogue made no sense. He was also getting more withdrawn than usual. He was watching TV or playing video games all night until the early hours and then working the next day. His parents noticed he wasn't making good eye contact with them and that he never smiled or showed any type of emotion other than anger when his beliefs were challenged.

When they told him they were taking him to a psychiatrist he didn't want to go. They told him if he wanted to continue living with them, he'd have to get assessed by a professional. He reluctantly agreed. He was diagnosed with paranoid schizophrenia.

His parents suspected as much but were still devastated. Their son, however, didn't seem to understand the diagnosis and felt the doctor and his parents didn't understand him. Brian reluctantly tried the antipsychotic medication but didn't like how he felt on it. It seemed to increase his appetite and it made him tired when he was working, so he stopped without letting his parents know. He told them he was taking it, but they didn't see any change in his behavior.

By the next year, he was certain his neighbors were spying on him. He confronted them. "Stop bothering me!"

"We don't know what you're talking about," they'd plead.

"Your daughter's harassing me!"

His accusations made them call the cops.

After evaluating Brian, they gave him two options. Go into a psychiatric facility or an outpatient program. Brian wasn't happy with either but took the latter to avoid a hospital stay. He could stay with his parents, who attended family sessions. They were referred to NAMI (National Association for Mental Illness) to understand their son's condition better. Brian still worked part-time from home.

A new psychiatrist agreed with the diagnosis and started him on an atypical antipsychotic medication. Brian liked it one better than the first because it helped him sleep but he didn't like feeling restless. Brian felt like he couldn't stop moving. This side effect is akathisia.

Brian started a second mood stabilizer: Lithium. He didn't enjoy the way it made him feel, either.

So, he stopped taking them, but didn't tell his parents or doctor. He kept his thoughts and feelings to himself to hide his decision. He made it through the program and was discharged. He learned to hide his emotions and feelings and didn't share the suspicions and paranoia.

Brian knew he was right and didn't care what anybody else thought. He knew his neighbors were getting away with their surveillance, so he kept an eye on them but didn't engage since he didn't want to go back to a treatment program.

He hated discussing his feelings or answering questions during individual or group sessions. This was confidential information he wanted to keep to himself. It was nobody's business. He didn't like getting controlled by the doctors and therapists, he felt, so he just said and did the minimum to get by and leave as soon as possible.

"I tried to hide that I'd stopped taking my meds by taking a large dose of lithium prior to getting my blood drawn," Brian admitted. "I thought I'd outsmarted them."

"Over the following month, we knew he'd fallen back into the patterns of isolating, muttering, ignoring his hygiene, avoiding eye contact, and showing little emotion," his mom said.

"We met folks at NAMI meetings who gave us your name. After we investigated you, we decided to make an appointment," his dad said.

Brian didn't want to see yet another doctor but relented when he learned it was mandatory to continue living with them.

During our first visit, I asked Brian, "Can you tell me about the voices?"

"I hear from the different women I like. They like me, too," he said. "They're from my video games."

"Do you think they're real?"

He looked embarrassed. "Yes. I know it sounds like I'm lying, but there's a mutual attraction. No one understands."

"Tell me more."

"Sometimes I hear the neighbors' voices, especially the man and his teenage daughter. They're spying on me."

"Why would they do that?" I asked.

"I'm not sure," Brian said. "There's definitely an ulterior motive, though."

"What do you think about the medications you've taken?" He was prescribed atypical antipsychotic medications and lithium.

"I don't like what I found on the internet," he said.

"Researching on the internet without guidance isn't a great idea," I explained. "You need proper training and knowledge. If we turn it around, I could never do what you do on the computer. I just don't have engineering or computer knowledge."

THE CORONA PROTOCOL   95

Brian smiled for the first time. "I just didn't like the idea of taking medications because it doesn't seem like there's anything wrong with me. They make me feel terrible. I don't think they're necessary."

Reviewing his symptoms showed his sleep was disrupted. "I can't shut my brain down at night. I stay up and watch TV or play video games. On weekends when I'm not working, I catch up on sleep before work on Monday."

I explained the role of genetics since his father's uncle was believed to be schizophrenic and his mother's grandmother had been institutionalized for several years. She was treated with electroconvulsive therapy as part of the treatment and died at a relatively young age. "Genetics seems to be the key factor in your case," I told him.

Brian's age of onset was typical and consistent for the condition.

I prescribed Seroquel, a dopamine antagonist that helps shut down dopamine. When taken at bedtime, it can dramatically help sleep patterns. I titrated it to a relatively high dose.

When Brian returned to my office, he was doing better. He showed a consistent sleep pattern and better daytime functioning.

He wasn't completely healed. He still had some delusional thinking. "It makes sense that some of the voices aren't real," he said. A good step forward.

Brian appeared more lucid and made more sense. Eye contact improved.

His parents were thrilled with the progress, but we weren't done. "With his level of mental illness, it's doubtful a single medication is enough. The rational poly-pharmaceutical approach is the best technique for this disorder."

I added Depakote ER, which modulates GABA and glutamate, titrating it to an elevated level.

By the visit a few weeks later, Brian appeared significantly better. He seemed to understand the voices weren't real but still struggled with for it to make sense.

"Exercise is important. Eat a well-balanced diet so as not to gain weight," I said. If he'd been obese and struggled with overeating, adding Topamax would be appropriate to help control his appetite and lose weight. If Seroquel had been too sedating, he'd be switched to a less sedating antipsychotic medication.

A few months later he was still doing much better. Brian's parents were thrilled with his progress and were happy he was engaging more with them and other family members.

He met people through work and socialized. He preferred to be alone but tried to get out. Work was going well, and he was praised by his supervisors as being a diligent worker.

I have seen many cases of schizophrenia that are not nearly as high functioning as Brian's, which is sad. Many cannot function in a work setting and there's a high incidence of drug addiction, homelessness, and suicide. Some can be violent and cause significant and permanent damage to others. Some smoke, eat poorly and adopt other unhealthy habits such as not exercising, which can lead to an increased risk of obesity, diabetes, cardiovascular disease, and early death.

They are at increased risk of ending up in jail due to drug use, often going hand-in-hand with crime. Prisons are our modern psychiatric hospitals, the vast majority struggle with mental illness.

Those in and out of prison and involved in the courts are notoriously noncompliant with treatment. An excellent choice available are monthly injections of antipsychotic medications. These are monitored and mandated by the courts. This helps keep these patients walking on a good path.

In contrast, most civilian patients can be managed with oral medications.

This is why Brian's case was so refreshing and exciting. Schizophrenia is a treatable illness with many excellent medications. I like to look at the positives and not dwell on the negatives. It's not a hopeless diagnosis but a hopeful one, as long as people in need receive the help they need. Brian and his parents couldn't agree more.

The good news is with proper treatment, compliance, family support and psychological support, schizophrenia is a diagnosis that one can live with and, in best cases, can thrive.

CHAPTER 8

Treatment Resistant Disorders

This is a broad category. Many people can be classified in this group. If a disorder is treatment-resistant, it means the diagnosis is incorrect or incomplete. When a person does not respond to treatment as the provider believes they should, we need to step back and reassess the situation. It's vital to ensure the diagnosis is correct in creating the best treatment plan.

I first became interested in psychology during my pre-med years at USC, then more so during medical school in New York. I became a family physician since it encompassed treating psychiatric conditions along with other areas, such as OB/GYN, pediatrics, adult medicine, geriatrics, and psychiatry. I wanted to be well-rounded and make as much of a difference as possible.

During my three-year family practice residency training program in downtown Los Angeles, I became familiar with the first 3 SSRIs: Prozac, Zoloft, and Paxil.

A year after I started my private practice in Orange County, a groundbreaking moment occurred that changed everything. Effexor XR was the first SNRI to balance serotonin and norepinephrine—the first dual-action medication.

With Effexor, I observed more of a physical connection and a better reduction of anxiety as compared with other SSRIs. Patient's physical complaints lessened.

Patients use of this new psychotropic medication showed a significant connection between the mind and body, and norepinephrine—not just serotonin—was key.

It was a mystery and a wonder, starting me on a journey that has continued to this day. I was blown away. Why had I not read about what I was seeing in books and journals, or hearing about it at lectures and conferences? Why hadn't other doctors recognized the emotional and physical connection?

There was more to explore as new medications arrived in the 1990s and into the new millennium.

I gave up traditional family medicine and focused on my technique: Mind-Body medicine.

At that time, primary care doctors focused on the physical body while neglecting the mental aspects. They ignored how the brain connects with the body. Meanwhile, psychiatrists understand the brain and mental aspects but don't appreciate the physical and somatic aspects and how those connect with the brain.

I understood the mind-body connection and why different specialties missed the bigger picture. They kept focused on their organs of choice.

The most important organ—the brain! —cannot be separated from the rest of the body. The nervous system connects to each part.

It was exciting discovering the connection and understanding its importance.

During the latter 1990s, I discovered why some patients were only slightly improving with antidepressants or getting worse. There lurked another diagnosis behind depression and/or anxiety.

In Chicago in 1997, a speaker training conference on lecturing about bipolar disorder to primary care doctors opened my eyes. What a game changer. Patients who only improved slightly better or got worse had variations of bipolar disorder. It presented in many different ways.

When I first heard that it takes 7 to 10 years and 3 to 4 doctors to accurately diagnose bipolar disorder, I was shocked and dismayed. Something was terribly wrong. I needed to do anything I could to change that.

At the turn of the millennium, I gave up traditional family medicine and began practicing a new specialty, mixing primary care and psychiatry. In treating patients with this different approach, it led to miraculous results.

Compelled to share my findings with a wider audience, I started my writing journey 20 years ago, which continues today.

I miss certain aspects of being a family doctor but never look back in regret. I knew what I needed to do. There was no choice.

It's been an exciting, sometimes difficult journey of discovery to figure out hidden secrets beneath the surface of the mind-body connection and the interaction between physical and emotional health. I've devoted the rest of my practice and life to exploring the subject, which still excites me. There's still a lot to learn and share.

FURTHER READING:

I discuss my story in more detail in part 5 of this book, as well as in my first book. I share more about variations in part 5 of this book and in chapter 11 "The Ups and Downs of Bipolar Disorder" in my first book.

Karen

After seeing several doctors, Karen became frustrated with the western medical approach. It only provided slight symptomatic relief but didn't give her any answers. She visited naturopaths and tried different herbs and supplements. All supplied only minimal relief.

One worked with her energy fields, sold her crystals and aromatic treatments, but felt no noticeable improvement. An acupuncturist gave her Chinese herbs and acupuncture treatments. She attended several chiropractic appointments for adjustments. Some treatments helped a bit but not enough to continue. Frustrated, Karen said, "I didn't think there was hope for me."

She was wrong.

"I heard from some friends you like challenging cases other providers can't solve. What do I have to lose?" she told me.

Karen filled out three pages on her intake form, including the fact she didn't like western medical approaches. What she didn't know was that I don't, either.

She filled three pages of notes on her intake form; it'd be a complex case. At our first appointment, she handed me a manila folder full of multiple medical information, including several labs, diagnostic studies, abdominal ultrasounds, CT scans, MRI scans, and dietary plans from nutritionists.

Karen brought her bag of supplements she'd taken for years. I noted each one carefully. "Have any of these helped?" I asked.

"Not sure," she said. "But I need to keep taking them, just in case."

"You've got a list of diagnoses."

"Yup. I have Fibromyalgia, Irritable Bowel Syndrome (IBS), chronic fatigue syndrome, acid reflux, headaches (migraine and muscular), chronic recurring insomnia, persistent neck, shoulder and upper back tension and spasm, and jaw pain from TMJ because I clench and grind my teeth. I wear a night guard." She continued, "I have lower back pain, scattered joint pains, and occasional numbness and tingling in my arms and legs. I saw a neurologist. They had nerve conduction studies done, which showed no obvious reason. I'm sure I have some type of autoimmune disease. Doesn't make sense why my blood tests come out normal."

After so many tests, why had she only experienced brief symptomatic relief? "Was it my imagination? I'm just not sure anymore."

She was beyond frustrated. After looking at the tests, supplements, and treatments, and reviewing her history, I knew exactly what was going on. "I can help you."

Karen looked at me suspiciously. "Not the first time I've heard that," she said. "I'll believe it when I see it."

"Great," I said. "I'll take you up on this challenge."

She had a fairly normal childhood, free of any abuse, but her parents got divorced when she was in elementary school. "I didn't understand why. They seemed fine. I thought it was my fault."

Karen developed anxiety, believing terrible things could happen beyond her control. She got headaches and stomach aches at school. At the nurse's office, she'd demand they call her mother so she could go home.

Her anxiety got worse in middle school.

Meanwhile, her parents worried about her problems, like the ever-worsening mood swings before her period. Sad and depressed, Karen had suicidal thoughts she hid. Occasionally, she showed severe anger outbursts with her parents and friends. "I couldn't control my temper."

Their pediatrician didn't have experience treating such issues and referred her to a psychiatrist specializing in adolescents.

The psychiatrist started Karen on the SSRI antidepressant Prozac.

Karen's parents and friends noticed a definite improvement, but she didn't like feeling tired, apathetic, and numb. She refused to take it and promised she was better and would change.

"We had our doubts," her mom said. "And Karen still had issues with depression and anxiety, as well as headaches and stomachaches. She got a bit better in her late teens and early 20s. She started to exercise more regularly to reduce her stress level."

"I also started yoga and meditation classes to learn how to relax when I needed. I tried to learn how to deal with stress by using whichever coping strategies worked for different situations," Karen said. "But I still had difficulty controlling my anger. I didn't understand why my moods were so up-and-down. I didn't know what was causing me so much distress and anger."

Karen began a new life in her mid-20s. "I was happy to get married and be a mother, but there was still something not right. I felt good during my first pregnancy, but then things took a turn for the worse. My OB/GYN prescribed an antidepressant for postpartum depression, but I didn't want that. When. I took one before, it was a disaster. I wanted a more natural solution that was good for me."

"I hear you," I said. "Go on."

"After my first pregnancy, I never felt back to my old self. I argued with my husband. Having a kid is stressful and I was always irritable and lashed out at them. I felt terrible after the meltdowns and would cry uncontrollably."

Somehow, she felt better during her second pregnancy. "I wasn't sure why."

This can happen during pregnancy and is known as the pregnancy glow. There's an abrupt hormonal change. Pregnant women have a high estrogen level and no longer have fluctuating hormone cycles as a they do while menstruating.

For example, the first couple of weeks of the menstrual cycle has the highest estrogen level. Ovulation occurs about two weeks after the start of the cycle, which is also about two weeks prior to the next period.

After ovulation, estrogen levels decrease, resulting in some women experiencing negative mood changes during those days. This is referred to as PMS (premenstrual syndrome) or more correctly referred to as PMDD (premenstrual dysphoric disorder). Some women notice negative mood changes and irritability days or even a week or two prior to menses. This can change abruptly, positively, after menses starts for the following two weeks until ovulation. The pattern repeats.

During pregnancy, these fluctuations don't occur. Their absence produces positive mood changes in some women, as was the case with Karen. After her second delivery, the positive changes in her mood during pregnancy dissipated. She fell into a deep depression, experienced anxiety, irritability, and angry outbursts. Again, her doctor urged her to try an antidepressant, but she refused, looking for a more "natural" solution.

Karen's family doctor had a lot of lab tests done, which were all within normal limits. Convinced they'd missed something; Karen wasn't sure why she felt terrible while the labs came back normal. "I was determined to get some answers. I knew the key was in switching from western medicine to naturopaths and other holistic providers. If they couldn't help me, that was it. I'd never feel better."

"Me and my husband weren't getting along again. Our relationship was a roller coaster and wanted to get off. We talked about separating, but decided to wait so we wouldn't put the kids through that. We were miserable, but we did our best to co-parent. Even with the threat of splitting up my family, I still had temper problems. Trivial things set me off."

Her family learned the signs when to get away and avoid her wrath and toxic words. She isolated even more, sensing they didn't want to be around her.

Getting up early and going to school by themselves, they'd scurry to their rooms after school to get away from any conflicts. They only went to the kitchen to grab food and go back into their rooms.

Her husband was used to her episodes, too. As soon as he saw a change, he'd get away. He slept in a separate room, saying he had to get up early for work and her snoring kept him up. That wasn't the reason.

Karen couldn't retain friends because of her toxic behavior. Most didn't have the patience to put up with her. Everyone she knew, including her parents, was affected by her negativity. She became angry at herself for the situation she'd gotten herself into. "I couldn't figure out a way to get out of that living hell."

Her lab results were typical for a patient with her history. Her panel was a CBC: a comprehensive chemistry panel. It included a thyroid panel, iron level, B12 and folic acid level, vitamin D level, testing for Epstein-Barr virus and Lyme disease, a mono test, a sedimentation rate and ANA (both for generalized inflammation and autoimmune disease, both negative), hormone levels, HIV and STD testing to make sure she hadn't caught something from her husband, whom she didn't trust, though they hadn't been intimate for some time. All her blood, urine, and saliva tests came out normal.

Karen had other tests: an ultrasound and CT scan of her abdomen due to ongoing abdominal pain. CT and MRI scans of her head to ensure she didn't have brain cancer due to her headaches; EKGs, a Holter monitor and a stress test for her history of chest pain and palpitations, and a nerve conduction study. All the test results were normal.

106

"Do you think we should run any of them again to be sure nothing was missed?" she asked.

"No," I said. "You've done more than enough. I know what's going on."

She looked at me suspiciously. "You do?"

I drew two neurons communicating and explained how the neurochemicals flow from cell to cell across the synapses. I showed her there were imbalances caused by leaking at the receptor sites of the cell membranes, causing the neurochemicals to go the wrong way. "That's why all the tests were normal. These imbalances cannot be tested for using traditional methods such as blood, urine, scanning, or DNA studies. This is a microscopic problem that can't be seen with the naked eye."

"What do we now?" she asked.

"The best way of figuring this out is through using a rational trial and error pharmaceutical approach. This is cutting-edge science that leads to the answers and results. In my experience, let's start by using the best medications I know about and monitor you. If it doesn't work, we might need to change the medication. Everyone reacts differently."

"Why did this happen to me?" Karen still needed a reason.

"I looked over your family history and there's a strong genetic component, which is the most common reason why these imbalances occur. Your father was an alcoholic. Alcoholism runs on his side of the family. Drinking is a form of self-medicating an underlying mood disorder. You told me you were sure your mother had depression and anxiety, and so do other members of her family."

When Karen was a child, she avoided her parents, especially when her father drank, and her mom was angry and moody. She'd go into her room and take out her frustration on her stuffed animals, and sometimes on her younger siblings.

She qualified for the second most important reason neurochemical imbalances happen: times of hormonal changes. This is why it got worse during puberty, pre-menstruation, postpartum (each pregnancy typically gets worse than the earlier one), pre- and perimenopause.

Pre and perimenopause begin in the late 30s into the 40s. It tends to get worse during and after full-blown menopause, when menstrual cycles stop, and hot flashes increase.

The third most crucial factor is situational stressors. They included her upbringing, years of feeling terrible, the separation from her husband, her relationship with her children, and her parents and friends. She'd felt suicidal off and on for years.

"You have the perfect storm," I said. "I suspect you have four out of four neurochemical imbalances. That's why your condition is so severe and has been unrelenting for years. You've never dealt with the underlying causes, which is why it hasn't gotten better. I suspect you have a fourth: neurochemical imbalances. You have imbalances of serotonin, norepinephrine, dopamine, and GABA/glutamate. That's why it'll take a combination of medications in to treat you completely."

"I'm not sure about psychotropic medications. Aren't those using the typical eastern approach?"

"Most western doctors are not adept at prescribing them. This is the true naturopathic and holistic approach in the way I define them. Psychotropic medications don't add chemicals. They balance neurochemicals already present that need help functioning correctly by moving in the right direction, at the right time and speed."

I assured her. "If you follow my approach, you'll get better faster and more completely than you might realize. You've got nothing to lose and plenty to gain."

"I'll think about it after I do some research," she said.

I've heard that line many times. It's never a good sign. "The internet can be more harmful than good. The sites aren't regulated by the FDA or any other government agencies, including sites that seem more 'medical.' There's a lot of negativity and discussion about horrible side effects, which are wildly exaggerated. For example, have you ever noticed how scary those commercials about pharmaceutical products are on TV? They are laughably ridiculous."

"I get it," she said.

"What about chat rooms and message boards? Those are real patients."

"But who are these people and how do they relate to you and your condition? People who had positive experiences are out living their lives and not complaining about their negative experiences."

It's not a good idea to get medical advice from family and friends. They may mean well, but they don't have the medical knowledge and training needed to give rational guidance.

I don't recommend getting medical recommendations from pharmacists. They understand medications more than most, but aren't clinicians, nor are they trained in medication applications, especially complex psychotropic drugs.

Pharmacies also may hand out a package insert: pages of negativity which can be scary to the untrained eye. I recommend going to the nearest trashcan and throwing it away. That's what doctors do. Getting bad advice can be dangerous, and sometimes fatal.

"I understand and trust you," she said.

I prescribed her the SNRI Pristiq ER. "This is different than the SSRI you tried before. It shouldn't give you any side effects. I expect only positive results." I showed her the diagram showing its dual action balancing serotonin and norepinephrine. "This will help your mood as well as your somatic, physical symptoms. We'll start with the lowest dose for the first four days and then increase it slowly."

After a week, Karen said she felt better emotionally and physically.

"Stay on the same dose until you come in next week," I said. "All is working well."

The one-week marker tells me if they're moving in the right direction. If not, we can stop those medications and begin something new. I make myself available via phone or email between appointments because I care. I've learned countless details about the titration and fine-tuning of each psychotropic medication. Attention to detail is vital.

I can make gametime decisions to medication adjustments in between visits to help patients feel better quickly. This individualized touch is not something patients are used to from other doctors.

"I thought this would take weeks," Karen reported during her next visit. "But I already feel better."

"That's a common myth. If it takes that long, it's not the right one."

Her anxiety and somatic symptoms significantly improved, so I kept her at the median dose instead of increasing it. We'd have the option later, need be.

She said, "I still feel depressed and unmotivated. Low energy."

"Let's try a dopamine boost and increase the norepinephrine with Wellbutrin XL. This combination is a Dynamic Duo of psychotropic medications, and the most basic one in The Corona Protocol."

She had good news soon enough. "I can't believe how much better I feel after adding those two. My anxiety is gone, and so are my headaches, TMJ pain, and all my body aches."

"Amazing," I said. "But even though you're doing great, you're not yet in full remission, our ultimate goal. You're having sleeping problems that have gotten worse."

Karen agreed. "I'm only getting about 3 to 4 hours a night, but I'm fine the next day. I don't feel tired. I function fine."

"What about suicidal ideation?"

"None."

Reviewing her history, symptoms, and rapid speech, I suspected she had bipolar spectrum disorder. More specifically, bipolar 2 disorder. Karen showed hypomania but not mania and she had a history of depression.

"Wellbutrin XL turns on dopamine during the day, but it also needed to be regulated and turned off or down when appropriate, such as during sleep."

She shook her head. "Not sure I want to add another medication."

"I get it, but you've trusted me up until now. It's important to treat your condition until it's completely gone."

"What are you thinking?" she asked.

"A dopamine antagonist, which is labeled an antipsychotic. You're not psychotic. These medications aren't just for schizophrenia. They're often used for bipolar disorder, too. I want you to keep functioning well and not take away your progress, but make you feel even better."

Karen responded quite well to the medication. She slept better and was more stable on one of the Tremendous Trios I combined.

Her family was amazed at the difference. They liked being around her. Her husband moved back into the bedroom and reignited their intimate relationship.

A month later, she had a bold question. "Do you think I can stop taking the supplements?"

"There's nothing in there you need to take. It's your call and the only way to know is seeing how you do after you stop taking them."

"Sounds like a plan."

Within a month after stopping them she saw no difference. "I'm just going to stick with the meds you gave me. It'll save me a lot of money and there's less pills to manage!"

After a few months, she slipped and appeared depressed. "It's not all the time, but it's there, and nothing like it was. Probably just situational."

"True. Not everything has to do with neurochemical imbalances. Life stressor can cause changes in one's mood. But with your history? It's likely something different."

"I've trusted you up to this point," she said.

"There can be cyclical changes over time with bipolar disorder. That seems to be what's happening. You have four imbalances, but you're only on three medications. The best choice is Lamictal. It's the only antidepressant that works on GABA/glutamate that's also a mood stabilizer. This will be your final medication, given your progress. In cases like yours, Lamictal's the last piece of the puzzle."

* * *

"I have good news," she told me a few months later. "My depression and anxiety lifted. I've been stable for two months."

Karen remained stable at the three-month and six-month checkpoints.

Lamictal's not the only choice in balancing GABA. Topamax is an amazing, unique medication I've worked with for 30 years. It's three actions reduce anxiety, somatic symptoms, and cravings to stress eat specific foods.

Gabapentin is another common drug in this class. It reduces anxiety and somatic symptoms but doesn't reduce cravings.

Depakote ER is reserved for severe bipolar disorder cases, as long as it's tolerated. All medication in these classes have potential side effects we need to watch for, but that's true in all fields of medicine.

If a patient is treatment resistant, it just means the wrong therapy was given for the wrong diagnosis. You may have noticed several similarities in this section with the bipolar disorder section in part one.

When antidepressant and anti-anxiety medications help patients get only partially better, or sometimes worse, it's a sign there's a missed bipolar component. Same goes for some cases of PTSD, eating disorders, severe OCD, and any other condition that's not responding to psychotropic medications as expected. In these cases, we need to step back for perspective. We may need to review their history and dig deeper.

*   *   *

It's not always about just the diagnosis and neurochemicals. We also need to analyze psychological factors and any potential need for specific types of psychotherapy. We also need to consider Personality Disorders, which I will address in part three.

In such patients, psychotropic medications may make little or no difference. We need to ensure they're exercising regularly and paying attention to healthy lifestyle habits.

I discuss psychotropic medications a great deal; it's my job to be fully educated concerning these extremely important medications.

It might be necessary to approach them differently, even combining medications in unusual ways. The medications necessitate working symbiotically, improving on each other.

Doctors prescribing medication using normal guidelines are not getting patients to full remission. They must learn the rational polypharmaceutical approach.

During my days as a family physician in the 1990s, I knew something important and special came with the arrival of new psychotropic medications. I quickly gained experience prescribing them.

When I combined medications together the results were shocking.

When I tried to look up in journals and textbooks reasons for mystery illnesses we've covered, I'd see Etiology Unknown. They didn't know the reason. I was surprised other doctors, in conferences and at lectures, weren't seeing the same results I had.

It was a combination of frustration and excitement leading to my decision at the turn of the millennium to move my practice in a different direction. I realized I really didn't have to give up primary care. It was part and parcel of treating the mind-body connection. I was reluctant to give up certain aspects of a typical primary care practice, but sometimes sacrifice is needed for the greater good.

I don't mean to sound too serious or morose here because it was not all sacrifice. It was also a lot of fun seeing the results and witnessing lives changed for the better. That never gets old.

As a child, I loved all types of intricate puzzles, with chess being my favorite. I realized in practice the field of medicine was closely related to solving puzzles.

This has been an exciting journey as I have discovered and learned more over time. We should never stop learning. That's the fun part.

FURTHER READING:

If you want to read more about this, check out the last chapter of my second book, "The Human Being: The Ultimate Living Puzzle."

There are also nuances and artistic features in this field of medicine, and I compare the human being to a work of art and living canvas we can improve upon in the last chapter of my first book, "The Art of Medicine."

PART THREE

The Impossible Disorders

Personality disorders are an endlessly fascinating subject. Personality is the expression of the individual "self" regarding unique perceptions and patterns of thinking, feeling, and responding to life's diverse stimuli and situations. Personality is the external projection of the self, an individual's inner life made visible through intangible actions, through which idiosyncratic characteristics are impressed on others. When a person is described, it's their personality and core.

Individuality is shaped by heredity, disciplines that promote physical health, and life experiences. In turn, our personalities dynamically influence our life's course.

Personality disorders are generally described as mental aberrations that cause people to behave in ways considered maladaptive or outside acceptable norms and range within one's culture. These disorders can be an emotional deficit, resulting in acting out and contrary, socially unacceptable coping behaviors.

Patients typically run into difficulties when handling life situations due to their rigid patterns of thinking and behaving, which affects every aspect of their lives, including social interactions, personal relationships, and school and work performance. The problems they meet often intensify an inherent unhealthy personality trait. Personality disorders usually begin in the teenage and early adult years, while others might decrease in intensity as one matures, or more likely, doesn't mature.

Personality disorders are grouped into three clusters based on their characteristics and symptoms. Many have multiple symptoms, and don't need every characteristic to be diagnosed.

Cluster A personality disorders are categorized by odd, eccentric thinking and behaviors. They include paranoid, schizoid, and schizotypal traits.

Cluster C personality disorders are characterized by anxious and fearful thinking and behaviors. These include avoidant, dependent, and obsessive-compulsive traits.

This chapter will focus on cluster B personality disorders, depicted by dramatic, overly emotional, or unpredictable thinking and behaviors. These include the narcissist, histrionic, borderline, and antisocial, also known as sociopaths and psychopaths.

The main causes of personality disorders are nature (genetics) and nurture (upbringing).

I refer to personality disorders as the impossible disorders because they're the most difficult psychiatric conditions to treat. They don't typically respond to psychotropic medications. Mood disorders can be associated with personality disorders, and medications can help take away the rough edges but don't resolve them completely.

Some patients don't recognize their personality's flawed because they're too close to the situation. It seems normal. There are treatments, such as psychotherapy, that can work if the person is open, but that's a big, "if."

CHAPTER 9

Narcissist

Narcissistic personality disorder is believed to make up about 1% of the population. More usual in men, women still comprise a sizable portion. Common among celebrities and those in power, such as those high on the corporate ladder and politicians, my best guess is 1% is a significant underestimation.

Unfortunately, this is becoming more common. Millennials and Gen Z'rs exhibit a sense of entitlement, a lack of respect for authority, and lack of impulse control, resulting in a lack of discipline and work ethic. It's a dramatic change from previous generations but will hopefully change.

Narcissists embody self-assurance, self-confidence, and self-esteem. Self is the center of the narcissist's world. It's all about them. They're self-important, lack empathy, and may enjoy watching others suffer. They like to win, no matter what the cost. Narcissists go farther to achieve their goals, feel entitled, privileged, and act like the rules don't apply to them.

The narcissist expects people to listen to him, value his opinion, and follow his orders. If you challenge him, he may get angry, dismiss his critics, or simply walk away and pretend he hadn't been listening. When placed in a position of power, he loves controlling others. He has a short fuse if challenged, so people avoid him. He blames others and doesn't take responsibility for his contribution to problems. He doesn't care about others' opinions and is a poor listener.

The reality about the narcissistic personality type is the paradoxical effect. They have an abysmal sense of self-adequacy but try to hide behind a facade. They fear people may find out the real him and not be impressed. The projection of bravado is intended to hide his insecurity and need for attention.

Notoriously immune from self-reflection and self-doubt, the narcissist is the little boy who never grew up past adolescence. Immaturity is their trademark.

They can turn from happy to sad, sad to angry, in an endless loop. They may throw temper tantrums and sometimes beg for sympathy and attention. Even though their emotions are volatile, they're shallow.

They're difficult to treat because they don't believe they have a problem. The harsh reality is they're unlikely to change.

Jordan

Jordan was an only child, and he liked it that way. He was a pampered child. His father was a successful attorney, but he always seemed to be miserable. His mother seemed to always be busy, constantly following orders from her husband, trying to please him as well as she could. His father did not pay much attention to him, for which he craved.

If he asked for something, it was given to him, no problem. If he asked for something and was told, "No" he'd throw a tantrum and make a scene until his mother or father relented.

He noticed his mother drinking more often over the years and avoided her more than his father. His mother feared his father; he emulated his father because he enjoyed feeling power over others.

During elementary school he noticed most of the kids didn't have as big a house or as many toys. He felt they were beneath him and were jealous. They weren't as smart and didn't do as well academically. He spent a lot of time studying and didn't like being around other kids after school.

He was not happy when he heard he was required to play a sport. His father said, "You're short and not athletic. You can thank your mother's side for that."

Jordan chose tennis where his size and strength weren't as critical. Even so? After playing for a few years, he was often beaten and relegated to the bottom rankings.

At one match, he got so frustrated he slammed his racket into pieces. His coach resigned from the match and chastised Jordan for his behavior. Jordan always hated his coach; he gave so much attention to the other players. He hated his teammates. They made fun of him behind his back.

His father wasn't surprised when Jordan said he wanted to quit.

Jordan was glad to get to high school. Unfortunately, many of the same students ended up with him. He wanted to put all the past memories behind, so he avoided the other kids he didn't like, which was basically everyone. He did well academically, since he spent a lot of time studying when he wasn't playing video games or on the internet.

Some guys received lots of attention from girls and other students, which frustrated Jordan. He was better than them.

"The football players are getting the most attention," he told his parents. "So, I'm going to try out."

His father laughed. "They won't take you. You're too small."

Determined to prove his father wrong, he signed up for the team.

He didn't fit in during tryouts and practices; he didn't want to make friends with any of the players because he felt they were just a bunch of stupid jocks and beneath him.

The coach put players into practice positions, assigning Jordan to holding the ball for the kicker on kickoffs, then seeing if he could excel at long snapping for punts. After a month, Jordan was fine holding the football for kickoff but wasn't achieving adequate accuracy in long snapping.

The other players snickered, made offhand comments, and talked behind his back. Frustrated, Jordan told his coach, "I'm quitting!"

His coach didn't protest.

From then on, Jordan kept away from, "Those stupid jocks and phony girls who hang around those meat heads all the time. I'm too good for them, anyway."

Glad when he finally graduated, Jordan was happy getting away from the kids and his parents.

He didn't want to think about his past. He proved his superiority to the other students academically with his GPA and SAT scores and was going to a better college than them. "Some of those loser football players didn't even go to college."

Jordan wished to follow in his father's footsteps and become an attorney. He majored in political science, noticing how well politicians did financially and how much control they wielded over other people's lives. Maybe he'd consider politics later since most politicians were also attorneys. His father made a lot of money and people respected and feared him. He just wouldn't make the mistake of marrying someone as stupid and useless as his mother.

In college, he dated, but not for long. He couldn't find a woman smart and mature like him. The students drank and partied, reminding him of high school and his alcoholic mother. He didn't like parties, preferring to study. It'd take focus to pass the LSAT and get into law school. Nobody would stop him from achieving his goals.

He saw how drunk and loud the other students were at football games or parties, so he avoided them. Those lowlifes didn't deserve his company. They weren't paying attention to him anyway and he didn't care.

Since he was smarter and better than them, he proved his superiority at graduation. But there was a kicker. Jordan barely passed the LSAT to get into law school. He didn't share his scores with his father, knowing he'd brag about how much better he did.

"Doesn't matter. I got in. I proved them all wrong," he said.

Busy as a first-year law student, he realized the other students were smart, but doubted they were as clever as him. He'd join study groups, but still preferred studying alone vs wasting his time with small talk.

He dated but never committed. It took too much time away from studying. He was at a higher level and wanted to be the best.

Again, he isolated, refusing social activities. Which was fine because he didn't like the other students. They were self-absorbed and shallow.

The guys were more successful with women than him, but he didn't care. He'd rather be alone than pursue women who reminded him of his mother.

During his third and final year, he rotated through different law specialties. He liked personal injury since it seemed an effortless way to make a lot of money shaking people down. He knew they were labeled ambulance chasers, and many were unscrupulous and unethical, but what did he care because he made a lot of money?

As tempting as becoming a personal injury attorney was, he settled for family law. He loved the conflict and drama when couples divorced and fought over their belongings and kids. He enjoyed inflicting suffering since, most of the time, he felt the men were the victims and the women were stupid and useless like his mother.

Since he enjoyed the rotation so much and got valuable feedback from the professor, he decided he could thrive in that area of law. He knew he'd do whatever it took to win a case, no matter how much suffering.

Jordan graduated from law school but failed the bar exam. He couldn't believe it. They must have scored it incorrectly.

He studied harder the next time, and came closer, but still didn't.

Angry his father seemed amused, and taking pleasure in telling Jordan he'd easily passed it his first time, he demanded his father hire a private tutor for his third try. He did and Jordan passed. Barely.

Jordan joined a family law firm and was determined to make his mark. He thought some of them were lazy, probably because some who had been in the practice for years were distracted with their wives and children, prioritizing them over work.

Since he put in so many hours, well above anybody else, he got a lot of attention. He spent a lot of time researching and billing his clients hourly, getting away with exaggerating his time spent on their cases. He deserved it because he helped his clients win.

He loved humiliating the spouses, especially women. These were his favorite cases to take on because they were the most fun. He'd use whichever tactics available, no matter if he was told he was going too far. He would get chastised by the judge for harassing whoever his enemy was, but he didn't care. He enjoyed it.

The senior associates said nothing to him, though they were told their junior attorney was inappropriate.

Jordan didn't care what they said. He was winning most of his cases and making a lot of money for them, as well as establishing a reputation for succeeding. He was the firm's busiest and hardest-working attorney, so they left him alone.

The firm hired a new paralegal, Lisa. She worked with him on some cases, and he could tell she was intelligent. He found her somewhat attractive. However, she did not come from a notable family. Even though she was the best paralegal he'd worked with, he reminded himself she was not intelligent enough to become an attorney.

He could tell she was attracted to him, but she found him to be distant. He didn't show much emotion or affection, so she felt special when she was able to get him to smile, though it seemed fake.

Lisa was surprised when he asked her out since she couldn't tell if he liked her or not. She felt special since she was chosen out of all the other paralegals and female attorneys at the office.

Over the following months, he spent more time with her, but only later in the evening since he often worked late.

Jordan expected her to do whatever he wanted when she had free time from work; she could do personal assistant work for him, though he did not pay her for the extra time and for duties she hadn't been hired for.

She tried her best to please him, since he seemed so mysterious, and she was intrigued. He didn't seem to have much experience with women, and she found out he only had short-term relationships.

The reality was he'd get what he could from a woman and move on. He was too busy and too important to waste his time other than getting sexual favors from women who bored him.

When he dated Lisa, he didn't like being around her family because of their low social status, and they weren't intelligent.

His parents didn't comment on her except to say she seemed to have a good head on her shoulders. He didn't care what they thought. He asked her to marry him, and she was struck it was so matter of fact. He assured her it would be worth it, and she'd be comfortably taken care of as long as he was taken care of to his satisfaction.

Lisa said, "Yes."

She felt special but had no idea what he really thought about her.

Jordan didn't see any other option at the time that would fit his requirements. Sure, she was beneath him in social status and intelligence, but she looked good on his arm at social events. She served a purpose.

He knew the other attorneys were talking about him. They knew Jordan was a vicious opponent in court, unafraid to cross ethical lines as long as he won.

After they were married, Jordan bought a 5,000-square-foot house in a nice neighborhood. Lisa was happy there'd be plenty of room to raise a family. He agreed to have children, but she was upset he wanted her to cut down her hours since she had a new home and needed to be available. It'd be a waste of money to hire a personal assistant, and since she had the time, she was perfect for the job.

Jordan expected the house to be spotless, so she made sure to keep things up to his standards.

Lisa missed doing her paralegal work but understood her husband was an important man. Helping him would be a better use of her time anyway. She told him she wanted to have kids, and he agreed but Jordan wanted to have a son to continue his family line and have someone to leave his estate to.

They had a son and daughter. Jordan seemed happy having a son but was disappointed when they had a daughter. People told him theirs was the "perfect family." He wanted to have another son but decided to stop because he didn't realize how expensive kids were, as well as intrusive when he wanted peace and quiet.

Lisa was concerned about who her husband had become, and how he treated her and their kids. She loved her new role as a mother. She enjoyed spending time doing more than just her husband's bidding. She could focus on them.

Jordan was getting upset with her for neglecting her duties and commitments elsewhere. "It's hard to do it all," she said. "I'm trying to do what was best for the kids."

"You'll have to make the time, and if you can't, I'll be disappointed," he said.

He called her stupid and other vile names if she couldn't prioritize his needs over the kids. "After all, I'm the breadwinner, and deserve it."

Jordan expected dinner to be ready when he came home and expected the kids to behave and to not cause him any stress. He would be upset if he came home and the toys weren't put away, or if there was any type of mess he could find. He couldn't figure out how she could let that happen since she had so much time at home all day doing nothing.

His kids tried to avoid their father because they didn't like how he made them feel. He was never affectionate to their mother, and he scared them: he often administered corporal punishment. He had a short fuse, so they tried not to say anything to set him off.

Lisa learned what to say and what not to say to avoid conflict. Jordan criticized her appearance when they went out. "You need to dress the part at functions. You reflect me and I don't want to be embarrassed. You're gaining weight and need to lose it right away. And don't talk to the attorneys. You never made it past paralegal."

Jordan preferred talking to the attorneys rather than their wives.

* * *

Lisa saw a doctor specializing in mental health after struggling with depression and anxiety. Her family and friends were concerned. The doctor saw by her worn look she'd been through a lot.

After a full evaluation including personal history, symptoms, family history, and habits, the doctor concluded she had severe depression and a significant anxiety disorder.

"I can make you feel better," the doctor told her.

Sure enough, she responded well to the correct cocktail of psychotropic medications. "I feel like my old self again," she said. "It's been too long."

Lisa had shown some symptoms in middle school and high school but dealt with them. Things worsened when she met her husband, got married, and had kids.

After hearing details about the years since, it was clear why she felt poorly. "Do you know what gaslighting means?" I asked.

"I've heard of it but I'm not really sure."

"It's a form of sustained psychological manipulation that causes the victim to question or doubt her or his sanity, judgment, memory, and perception of reality. The perpetrators make you question your sense of reality by sowing doubt as to what you actually experienced. They also persistently and blatantly lie to you but make you think that they are telling you the truth though you are pretty sure they are not."

Lisa couldn't believe what she was hearing.

"They make you feel insecure and enjoy breaking you down when you're not doing something right. They alienate you from people who care about you and worry about you. They want to control the narrative and simply to be in control. It's always about them and them alone."

"I think I should find out more," Lori said. After putting her paralegal research skills to clever use, she realized she was a victim and had to protect herself and her children.

Jordan had been pushing and shoving her, even hitting her once, causing her to call the police.

He denied doing so and claimed it was Lisa who'd hit him. He was just defending himself.

Since there were no marks on her and no physical proof, he got away with a warning.

After they left, his anger grew. There were several more instances of physical abuse, but Jordan had learned how to hide the evidence by not leaving marks.

His emotional abuse was constant, but she stood up for herself. He warned her he had a reputation to protect, and she better not talk about what was happening.

The kids evaded him, which was possible in their large house with lots of hiding places. When in his presence, they stayed quiet so as not to set him off.

Her mental health physician sent her to a psychologist to help with the emotional turmoil and to learn coping skills. He discussed the importance of a regular exercise program and a well-balanced diet.

Everyone agreed she needed to get out of her toxic marriage and protect her kids.

When he was served divorce papers, he was enraged. How dare she try to beat him at his own game. He was the best and would be more than happy to prove it. He'd won countless victories for his clients. "She'll rue the day. She'll never get the kids. I'll prove she's mentally unstable, taking tons of psychiatric medications."

Used to him calling her "crazy" and "psycho," she wasn't fazed.

He called her much worse when no one other than the kids were around.

Jordan did not like the change he saw in Lisa when she started talking back to him more and held her ground. He saw a confidence in her that he wasn't used to.

This was not the acquiescent woman he'd known. He was angry with her doctor for his role.

Lisa hated to admit she was hiding behind her confidence since she was still afraid of him. She'd seen what he'd done to many other women—she'd be his next victim. Jordan destroyed other's lives without a second thought, and he enjoyed the destruction.

He told her he would not leave their home. She agreed because she had so many bad memories there and didn't want to stay. She decided to move into an apartment and keep the kids with her as much as she could. Her lawyer warned her that leaving the house would take away a bargaining chip and project weakness, which might not help with negotiations. However, she told her lawyer that she needed to get out of there. The kids liked their rooms and all the fancy toys and video games, but they didn't really have many good memories there except with their mother.

The preliminary agreement between the attorneys was that they'd share the kids.

Soon after she moved out, Jordan moved his girlfriend into their home. How long had that been going on? It seemed suspicious to quickly replace her. Lisa was surprised; she felt sorry for the woman and hoped she'd be okay.

Over the next year, things only worsened for Lisa and her two kids. She and her attorney received threatening letters, which she got used to. She knew the threats were empty, but she was still afraid of him because she knew what he was capable of. He often threatened that he would expose her mental illness and that she was too "crazy" and mentally imbalanced to care for his children.

Jordan requested he and his girlfriend take full custody of the kids. The judge denied Jordan's request. The judge understood Jordan's tactics and knew they wouldn't work in his court. The judge had also already spoken to the kids alone and knew what was really going on.

The judge ruled in Lisa's favor by granting her majority custody of the kids while he would get them every other weekend. Lisa was fortunate since that was right about the time when the pandemic happened, and the courts closed.

Jordan was enraged by the judge's ruling. He petitioned the court to change the decision and was frustrated with the judge. The reality was the judge knew him all too well and wasn't going to fall for his shady tactics.

Jordan took out his frustration on his kids and Lisa whenever possible. Over the next couple of years, the police were called to their home multiple times.

Jordan blamed Lisa for ruining his reputation. The judge had it out for him, and he knew the other lawyers were making fun of him behind his back. This reminded him of his school days earlier in his life that he tried to forget. He hated Lisa for turning the kids against him. She would pay.

There were several times his kids called the cops when he was being physical. Once, Jordan argued with his son, punishing him by taking the phone he'd paid for. His son said, "No" and ran away, hiding the phone in another room. The police officers came and forced the boy to give his father the phone. The boy would never forget the smug smile of satisfaction after the police officers left. He hated his father so much.

Other instances involved the kids refusing to go with their father at the designated drop-off spot. This led to another round of police coming and forcing the kids to follow the court order and go with their father. His daughter cried, kicked, and screamed each time, while his son remained sullen. They hated having to spend time with him and didn't like his girlfriend. She was trying hard to be nice, but they could see she was fake and weren't fooled.

They spent as much time in their rooms as possible, but they couldn't avoid their father forever.

The kids noticed Jordan and his girlfriend would get into intense arguments, and they suspected it'd gotten physical more than once. They could tell by the changes they saw in her: the same changes they'd seen in their mother before she was freed and liberated from her old life.

At the request of Lisa's attorney, her doctor wrote a letter about her psychiatric diagnosis and treatment plan in full support of her mental health. The medication combination rebalanced her neurochemistry to the point where she was mentally, physically, and emotionally healthy. He'd seen her with her kids and knew her family well because many were his patients. She was a good mother, and the doctor gave her his highest recommendation to the court.

Jordan tried petitioning the judge's decision by asking for full custody, but the judge dismissed his petition for lack of foundation and evidence. The judge continued the same arrangement. He chastised and warned Jordan that he expected much better behavior from him. If not, there'd be consequences. This angered Jordan to no end. He promised himself he'd get revenge somehow.

Lisa became concerned because her son was entering his teens and was getting emotional and combative at times. What she saw scared her because she started to see signs that he was becoming just like his father. He would get violent with both, but especially her because she knew that he was afraid of his father.

The boy had been followed by a psychiatrist and was on an antidepressant when he came to see his mother's doctor for a second opinion since he was not doing well. The psychiatrist didn't make any changes and seemed to dismiss her concerns. He told her he was just, "Going through a phase."

Lisa took him to the mental health specialist that provided her with excellent results. His mother had been concerned that he had been acting like his father and didn't want her son to continue down that road. After the doctor fully assessed him with a longitudinal and complete history, reiterating what the earlier doctor found, he added a mild mood stabilizer to the antidepressant. It worked quickly, decreasing his anger, and improving his overall mood.

He was doing much better with treatment and was much more confident when dealing with his father. Instead of getting emotional and running away, he would stand up to his father and not put up with the harassment and abuse anymore. Jordan noticed the difference and discovered by finding his son's bottle that he was taking a new medication. This reminded him of the change he saw in Lisa when she started taking medications and became more confident and stood up to him, as he now saw his son doing.

As soon as he found out that it was the same doctor that was treating Lisa and had also given her the letter for court in support of her custody of the kids, this made him angry. He contacted the doctor's office and demanded that he get records of his son's visits. He was unhappy when he was told that they needed to follow the HIPAA guidelines and that he needed to wait for the proper legal procedures. Jordan threatened the doctor that if he did not get the records immediately that he would report him to the Medical Board. Even though he received the records promptly as per proper procedure, he reported the doctor anyway. He cited the reason as he and Lisa had joint custody when it came to medical treatment of their kids, and he demanded his son return to the previous doctor. He reported the doctor to the medical board for not consulting with him before he gave his son the medication. The doctor wasn't made aware there was any such agreement.

When he informed Lisa he'd been reported, she was upset. Jordan had never been interested in any of the kid's visits with the doctors previously. The doctor wrote back to the medical board saying he was unaware of any agreement and pointed out the medication he added had significantly changed the boy's life. Lisa felt guilty and volunteered to write a letter, but her doctor was sure his explanation was enough. It ended up it was.

Lisa was so happy her son was doing significantly better with the new medication, which stabilized his mood. His previous doctor was surprised to see the result, too, since he'd not identified the diagnosis. He hadn't got an adequate family history. He hadn't picked up that the first medication helped but he wasn't stable.

The good news? Lisa and her kids made considerable progress with medical treatment, psychotherapy, and a loving support system through her family and friends. Even Jordan's parents visited their grandkids.

Jordan hated his parents being friendly with Lisa. They knew their son all too well.

Lisa understands Jordan won't change because he's a narcissist. With the doctor's guidance, she read the material her doctor recommended. Jordan fit the description perfectly.

She changed her situation and was finally free.

Lisa found out Jordan's girlfriend left him. She'd figured him out much sooner than Lisa had. Now, Jordan lives in the house alone and is angry he must pay so much for child and spousal support. He feels taking care of the kids is lazy work and she does nothing useful all day and doesn't deserve so much of his hard-earned money.

It makes no sense to Jordan that Lisa's attorney and the judge beat him. How could they do this to him when he's so much smarter and better than them? He's convinced he'll get revenge somehow and they'll all pay. Even after all he's been through, Jordan's not humbled.

CHAPTER 10

Histrionic

The histrionic personality type constantly tries to draw attention to herself or himself, though it's more common in women. Receiving attention from others is a desperate need. Different attention-seeking behaviors include expressing excessive emotion and exaggerated hand gestures and body language when talking. They may be flirtatious and seductive and can be the life of the party, but sometimes shine too bright. They have little fear of being loud and inappropriate in public and can use that against others who don't want to draw attention to themselves.

Often, hypochondriacs coexist with the histrionic. They tend to exaggerate symptoms and perceive minor problems as major ones for no logical reason. They seek medical attention more often than necessary. They are drama queens, and everything is a crisis on which they thrive.

Crystal

Crystal was the youngest of five children. Her parents were older by the time they had her, and they were tired by then. The only way she could get their attention was to misbehave and make a scene. Eventually, they'd relent, and she'd get whatever she wanted and felt she deserved. Her older siblings and parents got tired of arguing with her because she'd never give up and would wear them down. She found it was the only way to get the attention she craved.

Everyone told her how talented she was, but she didn't think her family understood her star potential. She'd prove them wrong.

She dedicated herself to singing and dancing in grade school. By middle school, she had problems getting along with the other girls, especially those getting more attention. This enraged her, jealously thinking the other girls were prettier and more talented.

But then? Crystal laughed at herself. "How can I even entertain such foolish notions. I'm better than them. It isn't fair they're getting more attention than me."

Crystal's headaches increased. She'd had them since puberty, along with stomach aches and severe menstrual cramping. "I was always in the nurse's office. Sometimes she let me go home. I knew what to do to fool her, too, when I wanted. It was pretty easy," she said.

Her doctor determined there was nothing wrong with her and her symptoms could be emotionally related. In high school, she complained less about her earlier symptoms. She didn't like spending time at home. She tried to fit in with the theater crowd but didn't seem to get the best roles. "How could I show them how much I could shine?"

She knew she was at least as pretty as the other girls and got plenty of attention from the boys. They'd hang out with her for a short time, and then split. As hard as she tried, she never got the attention and praise she thought she deserved. They didn't appreciate her and took her for granted. She would show them.

In college, she tried out by singing and dancing. Crystal was invited to join the drama club. With many talented people from surrounding high schools, she tried to outperform them but was disappointed. They also didn't appreciate how much talent she brought to the table. "They were missing out," she said. She'd participate in the performances but didn't get much stage time, playing supporting roles.

Soon, the others noticed her mood swings. She was a drama queen, but not in the way they wanted. It became clear they didn't want her in the club. She hoped college would be different and she'd get a fresh start with people who didn't know her.

Crystal switched to major in Communications. She pictured herself playing a leading role in front of the camera. After graduation, she looked for work. The best she could find was a job selling paper products. She felt she was the most qualified since she had a college degree, which not all of them had. She knew she couldn't stay at the company long. She was too good for the place. She had so much more potential, and she'd prove that to them.

She returned to the family doctor for a recurrence of headaches and stomachaches, but the testing was normal. Her clean bill of health didn't make sense. "My symptoms were real," she said.

Crystal's doctor had heard of my reputation treating complicated cases, specifically emotional and physical disorders. He filled me in, and I scheduled her at once. Her intake form provided a baseline understanding. Her headaches and irritable bowel syndrome were due to stress, likely due to unbalanced chemicals within her nervous system. I sensed more going on under the surface.

I sensed Crystal probably had histrionic personality disorder by her dramatic history and gestures. "I've been to the ER several times thinking I was having a heart attack, a stroke, or brain cancer. They told me it was nothing but I'm sure they missed a clue."

Reading their report, they believed whatever was happening was minor. They noted she was dramatic and over the top.

She was prescribed a tranquilizer and pain pill but was warned of their potentially addictive properties. She couldn't be on them long.

Crystal liked how she felt on them and hated running out. She'd go from one doctor to another, sometimes to urgent care centers or the ER, wherever she could get what she wanted and needed.

When she saw me, she was on a high quantity of the most potentially addictive benzodiazepine, a minor tranquilizer. She was mixing it with a potent opiate. She got them from different doctors and filled the prescriptions at different pharmacies.

"I won't prescribe you opiates but will refer you to an addiction specialist to help you get off them, or at least to a pain specialist to help manage your pain. I won't prescribe a benzodiazepine at such a high dose, but I'm willing to work with you to lower the dose slowly and carefully."

"Okay. I'm willing to work with you," she said.

I wasn't sure she was serious about following through with the plan.

She was probably distracted trying to figure out how she'd get the medications somewhere else. I drew her two neurons and explained how and why neurochemicals go out of balance and how easily it can be corrected.

Half-listening, she said, "I get it, but I don't want to take a daily medication."

"You're already taking more than one pill per day, which is a tranquilizer you're mixing with pain pills."

"That's different. Those make me feel better and I need them to function."

"I promise I can get you the same results in a healthier and more supportive way," I said. "Band-Aid medications only help for a short time, not the long haul."

She shook in her seat. "Please don't take away the pills. I really need them."

"We'll lower the dose gradually as your body tolerates," I said. "Soon, the real healing medications will kick in."

"It's taken so long to find stuff that works."

"The curative medications will get to the core of the problem and actually fix it, not just cover it up for a moment."

"Okay," she agreed. "Let's give it a go."

Over the next few visits, she seemed more relaxed. Her physical symptoms improved. "I'm still suffering. Some of my friends think I'm doing better, but they just don't understand," she said.

"Even after I put together your combination of psychotropic medications?" I asked.

"I can't cut back on the tranquilizers. Can you keep me at the level they're on? Maybe we should perform a new workup of my symptoms," she said.

"You've taken more than enough tests. They've been reviewed and it'd be a waste to look for something we already have the answer for," I said.

On later visits, the complaints remained constant. "Dr. Paul, this is the worst that I have ever felt."

"This is exactly what you've told me on previous visits," I said.

Crystal said, "No. But really, this time it's true."

I continued lowering the benzodiazepine to a more reasonable dosing regimen, but she always wanted more. I tried some nonaddictive medications to resolve her anxiety, but none worked as well as what she felt she needed.

"I recommend you follow up with a psychologist," I insisted.

"I've been to one, but it didn't help."

She didn't get what she needed from him.

I hand-picked a psychologist, someone I knew over many years, and who had the patience to deal with Crystal. "I told the psychologist I believe you have histrionic personality disorder. It's nothing to be ashamed of. You can't help what's going on. We know you have a strong family history given that your mother and grandmother were constantly sick and in pain. They self-medicated in their own ways."

Crystal shook her head. "Not sure you're right about that."

Despite finding the best cocktail of psychotropic medications, they only took away the rough edges of her personality. They reduced the symptoms, but medical and psychological interventions only go so far with this personality type. Psychotropic medications certainly play a significant role, but they don't change a person's core.

Over time, Crystal seemed to slowly get a bit better, but whenever she'd come in, airing the same complaints, she'd assure me, "Dr. Paul, this is not my histrionic. This is real."

For the histrionic, like the narcissist, it's difficult for them to substantially change. For that reason, I refer to personality disorders as impossible disorders because several things must be addressed to treat them adequately. The reality is that the odds are not good.

Since they do not want to admit anything's wrong with their personalities, why change? It's not impossible to change when someone admits they need help, take appropriate medications, have regular psychotherapy sessions, and take responsibility and attempt to change their lives for the better. It's not impossible to treat personality disorders, just nearly impossible.

FURTHER READING:

Learn more about histrionic disorders by reading Chapter 6 on personality disorders in my second book and listening to my podcasts.

CHAPTER 11

Borderline

In comparison to the histrionic, borderline personality disorder can be more damaging and toxic, and more impossible to resolve than most of the others. They're at high risk for creating conflict such as arguments, fistfights, lawsuits, or other ways they can harass and intimidate others into submission. It's safest avoiding these people as much as possible for your own sake. If they feel crossed or rejected, the need for revenge consumes them. They're not satisfied until their victims pay the price they deserve.

Borderline personality disorder is indicated by a prolonged and severe history of mental disturbance. They don't have a stable sense of self and are unsettled to their core. The majority (75%) are female. They frequently attempt to anchor themselves onto other people and fantasize about living happily ever after. It can be impossible to predict their moods, since sometimes they're way up and sometimes they're way down. They're often angry and irritable. Others describe being around them "...like walking on eggshells."

Borderliners come on strong. They're flirtatious and seductive. They get too serious too soon, falling in love by the end of the first date or the first time their eyes meet. When in pursuit, they may make outlandish gestures and come on too strong too soon, to the point that it gets scary. Stalkers are an example of those who likely have BPD. The term obsessive relationship pursuit also applies. They seek others they feel are powerful and stable, hoping they'll make their lives stable, which they can't accomplish alone.

Borderline patients tend to have problems with interpersonal relationships. They don't experience healthy bonds and become desperate when alienating people. Their desperation can lead to worse behaviors.

Their lives are drama and dysfunction. Their thinking is black and white, good or bad, love or hate, with little room between. Their erratic behaviors might include self-mutilation, such as "cutting," which gives a sense of pleasure, while getting the attention they desire.

Thinking and behaviors can be irrational, with one or more associated likely, such as depression, anxiety, bipolar disorder, PTSD and others. They have a high rate of suicidal ideation and completed suicides.

Movie characters as examples are Alex in *Fatal Attraction*, chillingly portrayed by Glen Close, Robin Williams in *One Hour Photo,* and Jim Carrey's disturbing Chip in *The Cable Guy.*

With many professional interactions with people with BPD, my best advice is to stay far away. Doing so may be impossible for close family members and certain friends. Consider yourself lucky if you're successful. Leave it to the professionals, though there's only so much we can do. As this section's title warns? It's nearly impossible.

Jasmine

When she was referred to me, Jasmine was in her mid-20s. The person who referred her was desperate for help. "She's seen several different doctors who didn't know how to treat her," he said.

"I really like helping challenging patients," I said.

Reading Jasmine's intake form, it was obvious she'd be tough.

During our first session, I asked, "Why'd you come see me? What's your story? Take me back to your childhood."

"Well, I'm the oldest of three children. The middle child's a boy named Eric and my youngest sibling's a girl, Suzy. I loved being an only child before they came and got a lot of attention from my parents and relatives. People were constantly telling me what a beautiful little girl I was."

"I see," I said.

"After Eric was born, I wasn't getting the attention I deserved. My parents fawned over him. Their first boy. My parents heard about the terrible twos and thought they were fortunate it wasn't so bad, but they weren't prepared for the terrible threes with me." Jasmine laughed.

She laughed. "Dad was already making plans about what sports Eric would play. Mom was so proud of him. My tantrums got worse because they weren't paying attention to me."

When little Suzy came, Jasmine was angry. "She was competition. I wasn't my father's only Princess anymore."

In elementary school she knew she was prettier than the other girls and they were jealous. The boys paid attention, which she preferred to hanging around stupid and jealous girls. "The boys knew how special I was."

Jasmine harbored a dark secret, though. "My uncle Jeffrey made me swear not to tell anyone. When I was younger, he gave me the attention I was missing. He told me he noticed how unique I was. He touched me and did other things I didn't understand. He said it was because I was such a special girl. He warned me not to tell anyone, especially my parents. Because they wouldn't understand. He'd buy me toys and things, whatever I wished for, if I let him do what he wanted."

She suspected her mother knew but didn't say anything. "Maybe she was jealous because her brother wasn't paying attention to her. Who knows? But I did promise my uncle I wouldn't tell anyone. At the time, I thought they'd just be jealous. He was my favorite uncle and I wanted him to be happy. I craved attention. By the end of middle school, my body changed. Boys were interested in being with me. They liked other girls, too, which made me upset. Why wasn't I enough? It was so unfair."

When her favorite uncle wasn't around as much and stopped showing her attention, she wondered why she wasn't special to him anymore. She believed it must've been her mother's fault, since she was so jealous.

Jasmine's parents told me she'd talk back to them and fight with her siblings. She'd scream and yell when they would not give her what she wanted. She got into fights at school with the other girls who were encroaching on her territory regarding the boys. She'd talk back to teachers and was frequently sent to the principal's office. Her parents were apologetic and didn't understand why she was acting this way. They were used to her temper tantrums, but things were getting worse.

They tried disciplining her by taking away her phone and limiting her internet and social media. She threw a fit each time until they relented. Her younger siblings were so goody-goody and were kissing up to her parents to get more from them. It was all so unfair. Nobody understood or loved her.

She knew what to do, though. Jasmine figured out what the boys in high school wanted. Jasmine didn't tell anybody her secret about the special relationship she had with her uncle, and what she had learned from him. What she didn't understand, though, was why the guys did not want to be with her long after she gave them what they wanted. She didn't understand why they wanted to be with girls who weren't as pretty as her and weren't putting out as much.

All those other girls didn't like to be around her because they were jealous of her, Jasmine theorized. She never considered it might be because she shared things about the other girls that weren't true, and the other girls found out.

She didn't comprehend why the boys didn't want to be around the drama and chaos that followed her everywhere.

Jasmine didn't realize the reason her parents paid more attention to her younger siblings was because she was so difficult to be around. She didn't have friends other than the revolving door of boys. It never dawned on her that she was the common denominator in her chaotic life and circumstances.

Jasmine knew other girls talked behind her back, calling her a tramp and a slut. "They just wanted the same success I enjoyed with guys" she shared.

She thought being a cheerleader would help and was upset when she didn't make the squad. Were the other girls spreading lies about her? Was it because the cheer coach was a teacher that she had previous confrontations with? It was all so unfair.

Jasmine spent more time alone in her room; she hated being around people.

Hiding the cuts on her arms by wearing long sleeves, her parents became concerned about their daughter's behavior of harming herself. When they insisted, she showed them, and they were surprised at how deep the cuts were. "It's nothing," she said to them. "It just makes me feel better."

"You need to see a doctor right away," her father demanded.

Their family doctor sent her to a therapist.

After a few sessions, the therapist told her parents their daughter was opening up. She felt she was depressed and had a lot of anger issues and recommended she see a psychiatrist. Her parents wondered if she was too young to consider a drastic step like medication, but they were willing to try.

Her parents were surprised at how short her first visit was, and that she walked out with prescriptions for an antidepressant and a tranquilizer for temper tantrums, which the doctor surmised was an anxiety attack. Her parents reluctantly filled the prescriptions, but after taking the antidepressant, Jasmine seemed to become more withdrawn, but at least she was quieter and making less of a scene.

Jasmine didn't like how she felt: flat and apathetic at times, while at other times, filled with rage.

After one such rage attack, her parents grounded her and took away her phone.

Jasmine found the medicine bottles and hid her pills.

She showed them the empty bottles. "I swallowed all of them. I'll do more if you don't give me back my phone."

They called 911 and she was rushed to the emergency room. Her stomach was pumped, but the ER staff found no evidence she swallowed any pills. They suspected it was a cry for attention but kept her overnight just in case. She was released in good condition in the morning without any detectable consequences.

Jasmine hated being at home, restricted to her room. She cut her arms. Blood flowed.

She got scared and showed her mother, who wrapped her arms in towels tightly. It was back to the emergency room.

After tending her wounds, the staff decided her erratic behavior and suicidal gestures warranted her admission to an adolescent psychiatric ward.

She begged her parents to let her out. "I didn't mean to try and kill myself. I don't belong here with these types of people."

Soon, the hospital psychiatrist discharged her with a different antidepressant. It didn't work and Jasmine stopped taking it as soon as she got home. "I won't cut myself anymore or take any more pills," she told them. "I don't want to go back to the hospital."

By the time I first saw her in her mid-20s, I noticed the patterns throughout her life. She cycled through relationships, always ending up with guys telling her they couldn't handle her. She brought too much drama.

Distressed about her most recent relationship, she gave me the rundown. "I met Anton at a bookstore browsing through the fantasy/sci-fi section. He was definitely attracted to me the second I asked him what books he was looking for. He seemed taken aback when I gave him my cell number. After he left, I followed him and put a book with a note on his windshield, basically asking him out."

Anton agreed to meet her for coffee, which led to dinner. By the second date they were intimate. "He was quite flattered that this attractive woman was so interested in him," she bragged.

Within weeks, Anton became concerned seeing her erratic moods, angry outbursts, and general irritability. First, she directed it at others, but soon turned on him. He lied and told her he and his ex-girlfriend decided to rekindle their relationship. Said it wasn't her, but she knew he was lying. They all lied, in the end. She didn't take it well. Within a month of seeing each other, he was out.

Anton believed he'd been gracious. Jasmine was angry, he knew, but what he didn't realize was how fortunate it was he got out safely. That was much better than some of her previous boyfriends experienced.

After dozens of expletive-filled, threatening and name-calling texts, he asked her to stop.

Jasmine followed him and sometimes she parked near his home and work. He knew she keyed his car and bashed in his front windshield the following week.

He called the police, reported her, and filed a restraining order.

Infuriated, Jasmine had run into problems with the law previously. There were restraining orders and threats of legal action, so she knew that she had to be careful.

Depressed and angry, she had another breakup to deal with.

Her condition isn't easy to treat. They don't view themselves as the problem, even when it's obvious. They blame others and make excuses for their behaviors. Psychotropic medications can smooth the rough edges by treating coexisting mood disorders, but their problematic personality traits persist.

Jasmine showed obvious symptoms of depression and anxiety, but I also detected a bipolar element. I had her on a combination of antidepressants and mood stabilizers, which helped stabilize her mood and rationalize her thinking. Her parents and siblings noticed a definite improvement in her mood; she didn't come across as harsh. However, this was only the first step toward getting her completely better.

"One of your diagnoses is borderline personality disorder," I said to her.

"I don't think that term fits me," she said, offended. "I have very good reasons for feeling how I do, considering what I've been through."

"I think you should try a specialized form of psychotherapy called dialectical behavioral therapy, or DBT. It's an intricate and lengthy type of psychotherapy that's well suited for BPD. You need to go to therapy for many reasons, one of which is because you were sexually abused by your uncle."

She lowered her head for a moment, but then looked back up. "Okay," she said. "I'm open."

"That's a good first step. There are some books on this topic like *Walking on Eggshells* and *I Hate You, Don't Leave Me*. Those titles sum up this topic well, don't they?"

In a perfect world, this condition should be treatable if these steps are taken, but it's usually not that easy. Many don't stick with treatment if it is going well and often self-destruct. The personality type is the inner being and core of a person, which can be difficult to change.

Their circle of people: friends, family, doctors, and therapists, can get tired of the abuse and bow out. In Jasmine's case, she's doing well. So, it's possible, and others who have this condition can also be successfully treated. I remain a hopeful optimist.

FURTHER READING:

I gave Jasmine my three books so she could gain a better understanding of borderline personality disorder. The most helpful is chapter six in my second book. Check it out if you'd like to know more.

CHAPTER 12

Antisocial

Antisocial personality disorder, better known as sociopaths or psychopaths, is the most impossible of impossible disorders.

All personality disorders are extremely challenging to treat. Patients don't see themselves as the problem: it's everyone else. If we can persuade them and explain the diagnoses, it's yet another challenge convincing them to accept treatment.

They're prone to disagree with long-term, extensive psychotherapy best suited to their diagnosis.

We're not just talking lay on the couch and tell me about your childhood type of therapy. The antisocial personality crosses the line of decency and uncovers an evil and immoral soul. The best hope for these individuals is a spiritual conversion and awakening; convincing them to understand and accept the need for substantial change.

An antisocial is someone whose thinking, reasoning, and judgment is severely impaired. They constantly misperceive situations and other people, then act according to their misperceptions.

There's something missing or off kilter in their brains, skewing their moral compass and treatment of others. It's all about them, a trait they share with narcissists.

These two personality types may coexist, making a dangerous combination.

They lack empathy and enjoy seeing others' pain and suffering, no matter if it's inflicted by themselves or someone else. They don't experience shame, regret, or remorse when they break the law or harm people, which isn't normal. They can't distinguish right from wrong because they don't have a moral compass. Their only concern is not getting caught.

The majority of antisocials are male, though there are plenty of females. They're not just criminals, thugs, grifters, and prisoners. Most are of the lower socioeconomic class. However, there's ample "white-collar" criminals such as bankers, finance workers, professors, doctors, politicians (which I think is quite common in that profession), and pastors who've learned to hide their cruelty behind a socially acceptable image.

They're cruel and risky to associate with. Most try to avoid conflict, but antisocials enjoy it. The more unsettled the victim, the calmer they are. If you try to punish or get revenge against an antisocial, be careful. They'll always go farther than you. People expect they'd be able to identify an antisocial easily, but that's not true. They can be so charming and convincing that you'd never guess what's really going on underneath.

The antisocial treats others as objects to be used and manipulated, not as human beings. They are radically self-centered. They are prone to violence, and they justify it, such as "She knows how to push my buttons," or "If she didn't say what she said, then I wouldn't have had to hit her."

PSYCHOPATH

Comparing psychopaths to sociopaths is a matter of severity. Psychopaths are who we think of as mass murderers and hardened criminals. They're the most extreme of the spectrum of antisocial personality disorders. Extremely egocentric, they're cold with shallow emotions, lack empathy, and are manipulative. They can murder someone for no reason and have no feelings of empathy or remorse about evil acts they've carried out.

Antisocial/Sociopaths/Psychopaths develop their abnormal personalities during adolescence and early adulthood. Their mental functions and behaviors are immature. There are several reasons why this occurs. It may be due to an underdeveloped or damaged prefrontal cortex, which is the area responsible for decision making and delayed gratification.

It's common that poor parenting is a major component. The absence of a father, childhood trauma such as emotional, physical, or sexual abuse, and other types of dysfunctions are associated. There can be a genetic predisposition, as well. Thus, nature and nurture can play roles in forming this abnormal, destructive personality type.

FURTHER READING:

Dr. Martha Stout, a Harvard-trained psychologist, wrote *The Sociopath Next Door*. Dr. Stout estimates they comprise 3% of the population. The good news is the rest of us outnumber them. We just need to learn to recognize them. After identifying one, Dr. Stout recommends you get far away and don't look back. Protect yourself and your loved ones by not engaging with them. At all. She also states sociopaths have no soul.

Steve

Steve was a third-grade teacher in a suburban town, a place known for its good schools, a bustling economy, and for being safe. You'd swear he was in his late 60s or early 70s since he'd gone gray and looked weathered, but he was in his early 50s.

The teachers, kids and parents knew him because he was so friendly and outgoing. He liked being called Stevie, his nickname from early childhood.

Some were a little put off because they thought he was too friendly, and a bit of a "close talker" who didn't respect acceptable social distancing. Some teachers thought he was friendly but was a bit "off." They couldn't pinpoint exactly how, though. He was successful in the classroom, and more parents wanted their kids in his class than seats were available. He was best known for his over-the-top friendliness, his dramatic bow ties, and his childish demeanor, given his age.

When the pandemic that started from the lab in Wuhan China hit the US and the rest of the world in early 2020, things changed drastically. Their school closed and switched to virtual home learning.

This made Stevie sad, since he loved the teaching as well as spending time with his students. He didn't like teaching online. Students and parents weren't happy with the arrangement, either.

Once it was discovered the virus was not a real threat to kids and teachers, but rather to the sickly elderly and those with severe medical problems, private and parochial schools opened up worldwide. Some didn't due to bureaucratic decisions made by those aligned with teachers' unions. Many parents turned to charter schools and private schools, and there was interest in homeschooling.

Numerous teachers were concerned about their union's decisions. Stevie volunteered to temporarily abandon his teaching spot and explore private tutoring. This was the best of all worlds. He made the same salary and could also charge for private instruction.

Countless kids weren't being taught adequately using Zoom by the public school system. Their grades and progress reflected that. Parents sought out his help homeschooling. He guided the parents on how they could tutor their kids.

He was happy to help so many parents by spending quality time with their kids. The parents thought he was friendly and personable, and he praised their kids as students and deserving of his knowledge and expertise. The pandemic was an excellent opportunity, despite the suffering of so many people.

It was a real gift to the mothers and fathers who were working from home or commuting. They felt comforted seeing Stevie's smiling face and unique bow ties. When the parents were out shopping, doing errands and personal appointments it was such a relief to have an adult at home that they could trust. Stevie always made a point to know exactly where the parents were when he spent time with their kids. He was good at hiding his secrets. He knew how to take his time and not rush things. He got to know the parents and kids well. He listened to them, comforted them, and learned their habits.

Once he gained their trust, Stevie told students that part of the school curriculum was health class learning about the human body. He pointed out and explained his anatomy and invited them to touch him to really understand. He asked if they would allow him to touch them to explain their anatomy.

In addition to his friendly demeanor, he gave generous gifts to kids, carrying a briefcase full of treats like candy bars,

Blow Pops, Tootsie Rolls, bubblegum, and small toys. After health class, which was considered bonus material since it wasn't part of the official curriculum, he rewarded them.

Steve told the children if they wanted treats and to keep him as their tutor, they mustn't say anything to their parents, their friends, or anybody else. It was their little secret; no one else would be able to understand. If they wanted the best grades, which would make their parents happy, they needed to do well in health class.

He told their parents he was giving them the treats because they were doing so well with their studies. He praised the parents for raising such intelligent and well-behaved children.

They beamed, feeling blessed having a teacher who cared so much for their kids.

As the year went on, parents were frustrated that the schools weren't reopening. It was already proven it was completely safe to do so. They were concerned their kids could need to get vaccinated before returning. Many parents researching this found it clear the risk from the vaccinations was much higher than the risks from the virus. They mostly agreed, giving vaccines to healthy young kids, and healthy adults and the elderly, made no sense.

Since most schools weren't reopening, many parents moved to a different local school or a different state with a more open approach to in-person teaching and learning.

Stevie was happy with the Los Angeles teacher's union's decision to continue the shutdowns through the fall of 2021. He felt fortunate that he lived in a city and state that kept the schools closed. He was so grateful for his good fortune to have the opportunity to continue his personalized approach to teaching kids.

As the school year wore on, his health classes became more advanced, requiring more one-on-one interactions exploring anatomy with the kids. The rewards increased, including video-game systems and other expensive gifts. He assured their parents they deserved whatever he gave them: their efforts and studies were going so well. All of them received A+ grades in health class.

The parents knew each other, since it was a friendly community filled with gossip and rumors. Certain parents became concerned that their kids' behavior had been changing. Some were getting angry and throwing temper tantrums. Their grades slipped in all classes taught through elementary school virtually or in person. Except for the private tutoring with Stevie.

Word spread something was going on with their kids, but they didn't know what. Many described it as common among school-aged kids who weren't seeing their friends and were stuck at home for way too long. That made sense to most of the parents. The parents of Stevie's students noticed a troubling pattern.

Their kids were acting out. One young girl grabbed her father's crotch and was later seen touching herself inappropriately. Another mother observed similar behaviors in her son. Their parents didn't understand why these behaviors were happening at such a young age. Meanwhile, their grades dropped.

The parents placed hidden cameras in their kids' rooms. Stevie was so friendly and well-loved; they couldn't conceive how he was harming their children. They needed to make sure by seeing for themselves what happened when their kids were alone with him.

The boy's mother gasped and held her hand to her mouth when she watched the footage. She couldn't believe what the man was doing to her son, and what he was having her son do to him. She wept and cried out. Obviously, it'd been going on for a while.

She called another mother to warn her. The timing was good. Stevie was in her house—at that moment—tutoring her daughter.

From her daughter's room, Stevie heard their conversation. "He did what? Oh my God. We need to tell someone. The police. Oh my God, he's here with her right now. I've got to go."

By the time she rushed into her daughter's room, the back door was open, and he'd gone. They called the police.

It took time for the police to locate his home. When they did, his apartment was empty, like nobody lived there.

* * *

Stevie lived frugally and kept his belongings light so he could get away quickly when needed. He'd faced a similar problem before.

Stevie travelled out of state to start over.

* * *

Jan and Jenny spoke after school about the new teacher who also offered reasonably priced private tutoring sessions. "He's in his early 50s? Are you sure? He looks much older than that," Jan said.

"Yes. Who knows? Teaching is hard. But he's so nice and friendly," Jenny said. "Did you see his adorable bow tie? His name is Jim. He likes to be called Jimmy. He told me it was his nickname since childhood. He has all his credentials papers about his training, with letters of recommendation from other parents."

Jan nodded. "I'm going to hire him, aren't you? Our schools are closed even though the majority of schools in this country and around the world are wide open. It's so ridiculous."

They were so fortunate they had such an experienced private tutor who was so nice and so friendly. There was something kind of odd about him that many people noticed, but they couldn't pinpoint exactly what.

Jimmy was happy to have a new beginning and help parents and their kids in his own, unique way.

Growing up, Jimmy's own private teacher had taught him so much. He was eager to give back what he'd learned and what'd given him so much pleasure. He just couldn't understand why others didn't understand him or the value of what he offered. He deserved it, and they deserved it, and that's all that really mattered.

He realized he'd been careless, though, and he'd try to be more careful this time.

PART FOUR

Societal Disorders

I realize the subtitle of this book is a bit long, but I had difficulty cutting any of the five societal disorders: Addiction, Bullying, Homelessness, School Shootings, and Suicide. There are other problems in our society that didn't make the cut, and not because they're less important, but because there's only so much room in a single book.

I strongly believe we're at a tipping point in our country. We simply cannot continue going in the same destructive direction we've been. We need substantial change.

The three root causes as I see them are:

1) Mental illness: This is vastly underrecognized, undertreated and mistreated. There's a lack of understanding that this is not only a psychological problem but also a medical problem that can be treated quite easily and effectively, though sadly, in most cases, it's not.

2) We have seen an erosion of basic morals and values. I've been sustained over the years by my Christian faith and belief in Judeo-Christian morals and values. The world's major religions emphasize love and practicing virtues. Some people

in this chapter may be cut off from their spiritual roots as a reason for their problems.

3) Government and bureaucracy have grown too large and are too involved in our lives. They're incompetent with most everything they do. Case in point? Our public education system is mostly corrupt. Can you name anything they do well? Me, either.

How can these problems be stopped? When studying personality disorders, we saw that the problems aren't treated correctly using conventional medical procedures or medications. Not everything that's broken can be fixed. However, most situations can be improved if we fix what we can. For instance, people diagnosed with histrionic personality disorder are inclined to have less control and exhibit worse behaviors if their condition is activated by physical or emotional distress.

Our coping resources are diminished when sleep deprived, anxious, angered, or grieving. Strong emotions can interfere with the rational and self-control functions of the frontal lobe of the brain. That's why we tend to make stupid remarks when we are engaged in heated arguments.

Personality disorders like the narcissist or antisocial person will demonstrate his or her worst behaviors when experiencing mental or emotional turmoil. Everyone benefits when they have greater control over their moods and can regulate their emotions when upset.

We'll review some of the most frightening and disturbing behaviors we've seen in the news or experienced firsthand. There are many social problems that can be resolved by enacting and enforcing new laws, raising public awareness, improving safety standards, and more.

There are other problems that resist correcting. Some seem inscrutable. What rational person can comprehend the mind of someone who takes an automatic rifle to an elementary school and opens fire? Disturbed people do disturbing things.

For our purposes, we'll explore potential causes for irrational and harmful behaviors and the possibility of applying knowledge in treating troubled minds as one part of a multifaceted system to address what's solvable.

CHAPTER 13

Addiction

Addiction is a psychological and physical inability to stop consuming a chemical, drug, activity, or substance, despite it causing psychological and physical harm. Addicts become dependent on substances or activities to cope with daily life.

There are distinct types of addictions, some of which may not be considered as addictive behaviors. These include gambling, over-exercising, overeating, overworking, excessive social media and internet use, disproportionate gaming, extreme shopping, sexual addiction, pornography, unnecessary tattooing and piercing, or any other behaviors that are disproportionate to healthy living.

The "classic" addictions commonly cited are alcohol, nicotine (smoking, chewing, or vaping), opiates such as heroin and the newer and deadlier fentanyl, cocaine, crack, methamphetamines, hallucinogens, inhalants such as nitrous oxide and others, marijuana, party drugs such as rave drugs, substances found at smoke shops (like Kratum and others), and excessive caffeine, not just coffee but energy drinks.

Prescription medications can be addictive, such as benzodiazepines/minor tranquilizers, opiates/pain pills, and misused ADD/ADHD stimulants.

Addictive substances trigger an outsized response when reaching the brain. Instead of a simple, pleasurable surge of dopamine, many abused drugs such as opiates, cocaine, nicotine, and behaviors cause dopamine to flood the reward pathway. Sometimes, there's up to ten times more dopamine than natural.

We need to watch for cross addiction or substituting one addiction for another. Some of the most common are nicotine, excessive caffeine such as power drinks, excessive exercise, high risk sports, overeating and gambling. There's a difference between recreational use and addiction.

Addiction leads to drug-seeking behaviors, uncontrolled use, and neglecting or losing interest in activities one used to enjoy. Instead, they abuse the substance or engage in addictive behaviors despite health consequences.

It's common to see problem relationships, often finding partners who point out the addiction. They continue the abuse, hiding their substance abuse, creating all sorts of difficulties in the work environment, and with life in general.

Addiction is a brain disease. People choose addictive substances and behaviors to self-medicate an underlying problem such as anxiety, depression, bipolar mood swings, ADD/ADHD, OCD, PTSD, eating disorders, and a host of other diagnoses.

The intention is to calm stress, boost mood, and feel better by escaping reality.

By asking specifically what someone likes about a certain substance or activity helps me to be able to figure out which type of mood disorder is being self-treated and which neurochemicals are likely to be off-track and in need of attention and balancing.

Psychotropic medications get to the root of the problem and rebalance chemicals that are out a balance for reasons that the individual has no control of. They're the best holistic, supportive, and curative treatment available. They're holistic because they help the body to heal itself. Once the mood's lifted, the anxiety relieved, and one physically feels better and stronger from within, the individual has a much better chance to resist the substance or activity. When there's an optimal balance of neurochemicals, they're more likely to beat the addiction and live a healthy life.

Genetic predisposition can lead to addiction. Even if addiction doesn't run through the family, we can trace hints of depression, anxiety, mood swings, and dysfunctional lives. Genetics does not necessarily predict what the specific addiction will be.

For the parent or grandparent, it may be alcohol and/or smoking. Current generations have many more choices of substances to abuse. Another factor can be psychological stressors that affect mood and lead to abuse and dependency. There might be psychological stressors and mood swings, too.

A last factor can be one's upbringing. Nature and nurture may be factors if there's a dysfunctional home with psychological, physical, or sexual abuse. In these cases, it's more likely the person will develop an addiction.

We shouldn't judge people struggling with addiction. It's often not something they can control. Treatment's goal is putting the person in charge by using psychological intervention and psychotropic medications.

FURTHER READING:

Addiction is also covered in my second book, chapter 5: "Mood and Addiction" and on my podcast.

Chase

Chase was first referred to me at the age of 22. He grew up in a small town, the youngest of three kids. He said, "My father drank a lot and was verbally and physically abusive to us. We learned to hide, which left our mom taking the brunt of his fury."

He and his older brother grew up. "As soon as we were big enough, we stuck up for my mom and told dad to leave her alone. He stopped using his hands but kept on being mentally and emotionally abusive to her. Our mother was meek and quiet, probably because she was afraid of saying anything to set him off."

Chase didn't remember his mother drinking. Instead, she turned to Valium and sleeping pills.

"I got good at staying away from my father, and then my mother. She didn't have much affection or love to give. She was always sad, crying when she thought no one could hear her."

She cared for them by feeding and clothing them, but the parenting stopped there. They fended for themselves. "Anything was better than being at home, so we stayed out as much as possible. My older siblings did their own thing and pretty much left me alone."

He tried to be like the cool kids and smoked cigarettes after school by sixth grade. "They tasted terrible at first but after a while I got used to them."

By eighth grade, he'd had his first beer and marijuana, which he liked. "Maybe a little too much," he said. "It wasn't long before I was drinking vodka, and tequila, smoking regularly at parties, after school and during the weekends. Then I started doing them on my own, which I dug the most."

His grades slipped in middle school and never recovered. His parents barely noticed his problems, especially his stress, anxiety, depression. "Substances helped temporarily. My anxiety was calmed with certain drugs and my depression lifted with others. When I combined them together correctly, I found relief. I grew dependent, and my friends were experiencing the same thing, so we thought it was only normal."

Chase ditched school often, which got reported to his parents. "Dad did a lot of yelling, but there usually weren't any consequences. Mom didn't say anything."

He would stay away from home by hanging out at other kids' houses. They drank, got high, and played video games, while paying little attention to schoolwork. It showed. Despite failing grades, they decided to graduate Chase anyway, since his situation was common in public school.

Chase's grandfather asked, "What're you going to do next?"

"I have no idea," Chase said. "I never really thought about it."

After graduating, Chase worked part time delivering pizzas and food deliveries.

He discovered other drugs such as hallucinogens like psilocybin (magic mushrooms), ecstasy, and cocaine, if he could afford it.

Most of his friends continued to live with their parents and didn't pay rent or contribute, since they felt entitled.

Girls would come and go but ultimately chose guys who had more going on and had future plans. This was fine with them since they were simply happy continuing to work just enough to pay for their drugs and alcohol as well as their video games.

Chase's parents rarely bothered him, which was fine with him. Some of his friend's parents would bother them about doing something else with their lives and trying to find a real career. He was glad that his parents weren't among them. Everything was going great until the pandemic hit.

When panic ensued and restaurants were forced to close, it didn't bother Chase. He lived rent-free, with food and laundry service provided, and no responsibilities. He didn't mind the shutdowns. He slept in, stayed out all night, and saw it as a gift.

He figured out how to file for unemployment, and the government also sent him regular stimulus checks.

When the restaurants started opening up for takeout and delivery orders, Chase saw no need to return to work since the free money was more than he'd earn working. What was the point? His friends took advantage of the bonanza too. With more free time and more free money, they explored other drugs.

A friend found a partial bottle of a strong pain pill from his father. They loved the relaxed feeling and discovered if the pills were crushed and used in the same way as cocaine, the effect was stronger. When that bottle ran out, they tried finding them from local dealers, but they were expensive.

The dealer said it'd be cheaper getting the "really good stuff." Chase told his friends how much heroin cost; some seemed wary. They'd heard scary stories about heroin.

The dealer said it had the same effects as the pills, but it was cheaper and more available.

Chase was afraid of needles, so he was hesitant. "The dealer told me I could smoke it, which seemed like a better plan. It hit harder than pills, but I loved it. I was so relaxed. We'd lay around and pass out. It was more intense than marijuana. The only thing was when it wore off, we didn't feel good at all until we did more. Pot helped with the comedown, but not the cravings."

One of his friends suggested they try injecting it, since he heard it was better. "I didn't want to, but they egged me on, saying I was being a baby by being afraid of needles. They swore the experience was more intense than smoking, so I gave in."

He found out. "It was more intense, but so was the comedown. We had bad cravings, body pains, nausea, sweating … we just felt terrible overall. But the next time? All that went away. It was worth it for the high. Nothing like it. So, of course, I tried a double dose, which felt so heavenly."

Chase shook his head, ashamed. "My friends noticed me having trouble breathing. I turned blue. They slapped me and tried CPR. They called 911. Medics came and administered Narcan. It brought me back."

In the emergency room, a doctor was also an addiction specialist. The next day, Chase was put on Suboxone. "I was happy I didn't feel the withdrawal effects from the heroin, but the pill was definitely not as good of a high." The specialist sensed Suboxone was only a temporary fix. Chase needed a more thorough evaluation of why he was self-medicating.

* * *

After getting referred to me, his evaluation revealed an anxiety disorder with depression, with a subtle bipolar element. Over the next few visits, I prescribed a combination of antidepressants and mood stabilizers, which made a significant difference. Chase was able to titrate the Suboxone to a lower dose. His addiction specialist's plan was to totally take him off the drug.

For the most part, Chase stopped using. He struggled stopping marijuana and alcohol, but promised he'd keep working on it. After the pandemic passed and places started opening up, Chase did well enough to hold a full-time job.

After visits with me and his psychologist we decided on a plan of action for his career. Chase wanted to go to trade school to become a plumber. I was so happy and proud of him. This was the real Chase, the man he was meant to be.

<u>Discussion:</u> Chase's story is not unique; this happens all too often. People self-medicate for a reason. They are calming their anxiety, boosting their mood out of depression, relaxing a brain that's manic or hypomanic, helping them sleep better, and helping them physically and emotionally. Usual factors of genetic predisposition played a part, with a difficult upbringing with parents fighting their own issues, and the start of addiction in puberty with "soft core" addictions such as nicotine, marijuana, and alcohol.

Some outgrow this stage and move on, while others get stuck. These substances can be "gateway" drugs to more potent choices like cocaine, methamphetamines, crack, and opiates like painkillers and heroin.

Thankfully, Chase wasn't exposed to fentanyl—the most recent major killer in the United States. It's typically sent from China to Mexico where the cartels can easily get it across our wide-open southern border.

Another common factor is people getting stuck in an immature state, correlating with the age the addictions take hold. Typically, this occurs during puberty, often during late elementary school, middle school, and early high school. If the addictions take hold and they move on to stronger drugs, it's more likely their maturity level gets stuck at that time of life and then does not progress easily.

Now it's common for people to switch to opiates by the by the late teens and early to mid-20s. Most overdose deaths involve opiates.

The introduction of strong opiates for acute and chronic pain was a blessing and a curse. Many take them appropriately as directed and are able to wean off of them after the pain is resolved. Some, however, take them for legitimate reasons and found them hard to stop. The withdrawal is so bad they feel they need to use it to survive and not feel sick. Some admit they don't like how they feel on them but can't get off if they want to.

Psychotropic medications offer a holistic solution addressing underlying mood disorders. Medications like Suboxone/Subutex (or methadone) help take away cravings and support withdrawal effects. Patients need to be weaned off them, though some stay on the low dose.

We can then address healthy living habits like exercising, relaxation techniques, psychotherapy, twelve-step groups, and the rehabilitation community. Addressing the issue in a multifactorial fashion can get people on track in their lives with regard to personal relationships, work, and play.

CHAPTER 14

Bullying

Bullying is the use of force, coercion, or threat to abuse, aggressively dominate, or intimidate. It's a repetitive and habitual behavior pattern. It involves an imbalance of physical and social power. Its aggressive conduct intended to hurt another physically, mentally, or emotionally.

Motives for bullying include envy and resentment. Some bullies are arrogant and narcissistic. The abuser may feel empowered while concealing shame. They may bully because of jealousy or because they themselves have been bullied.

Bullies may have depression, an anxiety disorder, bipolar disorder, or another mood disorder as a risk factor. They also may have a personality disorder such as narcissism. Borderline, antisocial (sociopaths) or a combination thereof.

Bullying can result from genetic predisposition or a brain abnormality. Some come from typical upbringings, though usually they're raised in families characterized by conflict and instability.

Kids who are bullied often show physical or emotional signs, such as being afraid to attend school, complaining of headaches, loss of appetite, a lack of interest in school activities, a reluctance to go out in public, and fear they may encounter their bullies.

Stacy

Stacy was 16 years old in 10th grade. She had mixed feelings when the pandemic hit, and schools closed. She'd been teased and taunted by a group of girls. Stacy was a straight-A student and active in the band, playing flute. She was often complemented by teachers for her hard work and dedication.

The girls teased her about being a "kiss ass" to the teachers, being a "four eyes," a geek, and for being slightly overweight. Stacy internalized what they said and kept quiet about it. They also made fun of her playing the flute by making a sexual comment. "Only geeks and nerds are in the band."

When the pandemic closed her school, virtual learning was introduced. Stacy didn't mind since she didn't have to face the girls but was taken by surprise by what happened next.

A vocal presence at school board meetings, Kim was well known in the community. Kim couldn't believe what she heard from other parents. Her daughter Stacy was in 10th grade and her son Luke was in eighth grade. Attending classes online, she saw some of the material being taught, and was beyond shocked.

"Some of the books the teenagers were assigned to read were basically pornography. What happened to all the classic books we read when I went to school?"

She said, "Elementary school students were being taught inappropriate content, including gender confusion, basically teaching boys and girls they can just wish themselves to be the opposite sex. I was beyond disturbed that children were exposed to puberty blockers and surgeries such as mastectomies, hysterectomies, and the removal of gonads. This was shocking to me and other parents."

The parents were concerned their kids were being over-sexualized. "This subject should be taught at home, or at least with parent involvement regarding what content is appropriate for certain ages."

Kim objected to teaching kids to hate this country rather than love its uniqueness and virtues. She learned about critical race theory. "It teaches kids that the color of one's skin is more important than the content of one's character, which goes completely against the teachings of Dr. Martin Luther King Jr., who believed that what matters is what's inside the person, not what's on the outside. Is he or she a good person? A loving and caring person? That's what matters, not something like the color of one's skin that a person has no control of."

Kim realized critical race theory and the concept of equity went completely against the gains made in the civil rights movement regarding equality, individual rights, and individual freedoms, no matter one's sex, one's race and one's creed.

Another poisonous concept she saw taught to kids was the 1619 project, which basically teaches that slavery was at the core of the founding of this nation. Kim knew the truth about American history and made sure her kids understood the principles of individual rights this country was founded on in 1776. "I wanted kids to understand there are good and bad elements to our history, but that the good far outweighs the bad. A good example is the abolition of slavery after the Civil War. As Winston Churchill famously said: 'Those who fail to learn from history are doomed to repeat it.'"

Other parents and school board members disagreed, paving the way for bullying and intimidation. Kim didn't mind criticism over her views—she'd grown accustomed to years of dealing with such reactions. The school board and other parents had a more "progressive" attitude, although

Kim thought was more "regressive." She didn't expect how it'd affect her kids.

Stacy tried keeping in touch with friends through social media but found things had turned ugly. The other kids made fun of her because of what her mother said. They called her family racists, since their mother opposed the racist content being taught.

They made fun of their mother for wanting certain books to not be included in the curricula and called them prudes.

The kids were glad they weren't going to school, since they really didn't want to face the other kids.

Stacy's friends didn't come to her defense because they didn't want to be labeled "racists," "white supremacists," and "prudes."

Luke was lonely but didn't want to leave the house and risk running into the other kids.

Sullen and withdrawn, the kids weren't their typical selves. Stacy wanted to ask her mother not to speak out so much. They understood she was passionate about fighting for them and the other kids, and they understood and agreed with what she said, but it made their lives harder.

Stacy cut herself in secret, wearing long sleeves to hide the scars. She didn't want to upset her mother. Luke earned good grades, but slipped once he spent more time escaping into video games.

Kim felt pressure from other parents and school board members. She knew it was difficult for her kids and felt bad but felt strongly about speaking out. The other parents who agreed were too nervous and embarrassed to get involved.

When the school partially reopened, Kim questioned why they couldn't fully reopen. "There was evidence in other states and around the world that keeping schools open was completely safe. There's not been one loss of life of any student or teacher reported."

Ridiculed by other parents who didn't agree with her, they trusted public health officials, teachers' unions, and politicians.

"Why do the kids have to wear masks, especially outside?" she asked. "There's no scientific proof masks work inside or outside. Why are we reopening in a hybrid model? There's no evidence from other states or around the world that it's needed. Schools should be fully reopened without restrictions."

The more Kim researched the pandemic response, listening to credible doctors and scientists with different views than public health officials, she was shocked the decisions being made weren't based on science at all. She was concerned about the vaccines being released without adequate testing and scientific data. They were a brand-new technology, and many well renowned scientists were concerned about their safety and efficacy.

Some doctors discussed successful, preliminary treatment strategies and the importance of natural immunity: the best way to get out of the pandemic. "Why weren't more people speaking out?" Kim asked. "This just doesn't feel like the America I grew up in."

When schools reopened, Stacy and Luke didn't want to go. They asked their mother if they could continue school from home. Stacy had seen on social media the girls were spreading rumors about her that she was, "a slut racist," and a "kiss ass" since teachers gave her such good grades.

They made fun of her mother for standing up against the school board, insisting the children not be over-sexualized by being exposed to indecent sexual content given as assigned reading.

Luke experienced similar resentment from a group of kids whose parents didn't like Kim's outspokenness.

Closed to hearing dissenting opinions, the board hated being reminded they worked for the parents and kids.

As the school reopened Kim and her kids realized they were fighting a futile battle. Stacy and Luke agreed they'd heard and experienced enough and didn't want to go back where the tormentors resided. Even though Kim and her husband could barely afford it they placed their kids into a local Christian school, where parents had a say in what their kids were being taught. Stacy and Luke were thankful and excited about having a fresh start with exciting possibilities.

CHAPTER 15

Homelessness

Homelessness means lacking stable and proper housing. Primary homelessness refers to living on the streets, while secondary homelessness refers to moving between temporary shelters, such as the houses of family and friends, and other emergency accommodations. Tertiary homelessness refers to living in private boarding homes without a private bathroom or assurance of permanence. Another definition means those sleeping in public or private places not designed for use as regular sleeping accommodation for human beings.

The homeless are often unable to acquire and support regular, secure, and adequate housing due to inconsistent or lacking income. Homelessness is interrelated with poverty. Most homeless are single men, with the median age being 35. However, there are also too many women and children and families who are homeless, many victims of abuse seeking escape.

Homelessness has been a worldwide problem for centuries. In this country, there was an increase in the 1930s after the Great Depression, and later during the deinstitutionalization of mental health patients in the 1960s and 1970s. Homelessness rose during the 1980s and continues to be a huge issue.

There are factors besides poverty and forced evictions. Some include severe and untreated mental illness and those with an elevated risk of substance abuse. Both are interrelated, since most addiction is driven by an underlying mood disorder, they're attempting to self-medicate.

Being homeless comes with a considerable risk of suicide and overdose. Many addicts die from opiate overdose.

Homeless people have a substantial risk of adverse medical problems like infections, lung disease, and more. With limited access to resources, they're disengaged from health services, making them more vulnerable.

Some become homeless after foreclosures and forced evictions, and who do not have a moving plan. The government sometimes forces people to move because of a project that destroys homes to make way for infrastructure and gentrification.

Some have trouble transitioning out of foster care and other public systems. Others might be afflicted with disabilities, are migrants, newly released prisoners reentering society, have traumatic brain injuries, or have personality disorders.

Mental illness can be associated with conditions like depression, anxiety, bipolar spectrum disorder, and others. There is a high incidence of schizophrenia. Others have schizoaffective disorder and bipolar one disorder. Many are veterans, often suffering from PTSD.

Some are couch surfers, some live in inexpensive motels, and some are just squatters taking over unoccupied units. Some live in tent cities and shantytowns, or in the mountains and out in nature, using tunnels for shelter. There are those who choose to be homeless, preferring the lifestyle and don't want to change.

There are many challenges, such as hygiene and finding sanitary facilities, hostility from the public and laws against vagrancy, and their contact with friends and family. They may be unable to access government services without a permanent location or mailing address. They face exposure to extreme cold or extreme heat, violence, abuse, nowhere safe to store necessary medications, and safekeeping of bedding, clothes, and other possessions. Everything needs to be carried at all times.

Homeless kids have limited access to education and have difficulty with interpersonal relationships.

Seen as not suitable for employment, there's reduced access to banking services, communications technology, and healthcare including mental health, medical health, and dental health.

They have trust issues in seeking help. There's a stigma they have to live with. Some go into prostitution and crime to make money to support their drug habits. This is a dangerous lifestyle no one should endure.

Several organizations provide help for homeless people. These services supply food, shelter, a bed, and sometimes clothing. I believe private organizations, private donors, non-profits, and churches staffed with volunteers are more effective, efficient, and cost-effective when compared to government services. Some organizations help homeless people get jobs. Many of the homeless panhandle, but it's outlawed in some areas.

I believe the most important services are mental health care and addiction treatment. If we get to the core of the problem and treat the likely causes of homelessness, it bodes well for those suffering.

Our prison systems are our modern mental health facilities, only with extremely poor psychiatric care. A prisoner's life expectancy is 30 years less, with most living into their late 40s instead of their late 70s.

Even though the situation is grim, if we work toward the same goals, we can resolve this problem for the last time.

Billy

"One of my first memories is of my dad yelling and pushing my mom," Billy said. "Even then, I wished I could help instead of just watching."

Billy's rough childhood is an example of an unfortunate case for many.

At 2 to 3 years old, Billy discovered he didn't like hearing, "No," and got angry when he heard it. "That's also when Dad began hitting me. Sometimes I knew I did something wrong, but not always. I wasn't sure why he was hitting me. He did get more violent when he drank, though."

As Billy got a little older, he learned a trick. "I avoided him as much as possible. I wanted to help Mom, but she didn't want the help. She wanted to stay quiet and not bother Dad. That much I knew. I found her secret stash of pills, which were mostly tranquilizers. If they helped her, they'd probably help me."

He'd take some, but only a couple, afraid she'd notice. "I figured she didn't want to drink like dad. He wanted a second child, but I found her birth control pills. She told him she was just too old. I think she felt guilty bringing me into this chaos and didn't want another kid to suffer."

Billy was a loner and didn't feel comfortable opening up to people he didn't know. He did well in school and was an avid reader. "I'd fantasize about being Indiana Jones and experiencing what Indy would. I loved science fiction because of the aliens. I loved *E.T.*, *Close Encounters of the Third Kind* and *Willy Wonka and the Chocolate Factory*. I wished I could be Charlie, going through different adventures after finding the golden ticket."

186

By middle school, he found friends who smoked pot. Some ditched school all day. "Dad had so much alcohol, he didn't miss a stray bottle or a pack of cigarettes here and there. I traded bottles of alcohol for drugs. We'd hang. Listen to music. It was a good time."

He didn't really like alcohol at that young age; he preferred weed. "When I got a little older, I started liking beer, but didn't want to hit the hard stuff like dad."

His father was less violent when he got drunk and just slept a lot by the time Billy was in high school. He had a back injury after falling off a ladder. "Pretty sure he was drunk, or hung over, when he lost his balance. He was taking pain pills, which really mellowed him out, especially when he took them with alcohol."

He recalled a rough incident. "My dad was about to hit my mom, but I got between. Told him to stop or else. When my dad asked me what that meant, I told him I'd call the cops. Sensing a fight, he backed down. I was never close to him, so I didn't care too much. He never said he loved me or was proud of me. It was hard to care when I found out he had cirrhosis, diabetes, hypertension, and heart disease. They put him on medication and told him to stop drinking. He didn't."

Keith was closer to his mother despite her being emotionally absent. "She was self-medicating, but I needed more from her. I wasn't sure why she stayed with my dad, but I guess that was all she knew."

At least his father's physical abuse lessened due to his being weakened and drugged. "He still said nasty, horrible things to her no husband should ever be calling his wife."

Billy got into cocaine around then. "Coke made my mind race. Mushrooms transported me into a different world. I'd get so many creative ideas. I thought about writing a series of children's books where kids make their wishes and dreams come true."

After high school, Billy worked at a deli, selling weed, and trading it for other drugs on occasion. His parents didn't seem concerned as Billy supported himself. He lived at home, and they didn't pressure him. The arguing had died down since his father was either drinking or sleeping most of the time.

He spent less time with his friends and more time reading science fiction novels. "Aliens revealed themselves to me and told me about my purpose and being chosen for greatness. He got information he passed to others to keep them safe, even though they were under surveillance," he claimed. "Be careful who you give information to."

Billy suspected his parents were listening to him. He scoured the place for recording devices. His parents denied knowing anything about it, but he didn't believe them.

Electrical activity inside the walls unnerved him. "Was it aliens or the government monitoring me?" and couldn't tell if he was being monitored by the government or if the aliens were trying to communicate with him. He would take a hammer and bash through certain parts of the wall in his room looking for clues that he was being spied on. His parents would ask what the banging was, and he told them he was just hanging up art. In reality he put up posters covering the holes and hiding what he was doing.

He knew the aliens were protecting him and he needed to trust them. He knew he had a mission to carry out and it was worth the risks. Others would try to harm him in order to get a hold of the alien's classified information. He was always under threat, but he was willing to sacrifice himself to carry the message. He could save humanity.

By the time he was 23, his father's health got even worse. His cirrhosis deteriorated. He suffered heart attacks, causing him heart failure. He had so much edema of the abdomen they needed to drain the fluid with a large syringe. and his legs would often fill up with fluid. He wasn't in good enough health to consider a liver transplant. Advised again to stop drinking and using drugs, it angered him. The following day, he doubled down on both.

When his body was discovered the next day in his bed it was already cold. The paramedics couldn't tell if he'd had a heart attack during sleep, but they couldn't rule out the possibility it was due to an overdose of opiates mixed with alcohol. Was it accidental or purposeful? They weren't positive.

"I didn't feel anything when dad died, or even at the funeral. Mom seemed a bit more like her old self when he was younger. She seemed happier," he said.

Billy lived with his mother until she decided to move out of state, and back to where she grew up with family. She was another Californian who figured out they'd get more for their money in another state.

Billy told her he'd stay with a friend after learning she was selling the house. Billy assured her he was making enough money. She said, "Let me know if you need anything."

He knew she loved him, but she never expressed it. Billy felt a bit awkward saying goodbye. Even though he wasn't sure when he'd see her again, he said, "I'll be fine on my own."

By 23, Billy wasn't comfortable with the number of roommates when he moved to Los Angeles. "I spent a lot of time outdoors. Even though it's a big city, I was able to be alone. Then, there were protests and people wearing masks. I was confused at first but was simply happy to be left alone and not get too close to anyone."

Billy worked odd jobs, but mostly sold weed and drugs, holding some back for himself.

Preferring the outdoors to the cramped apartment, he slept outside in the vast parks. He got a tent and loved the freedom. Deep in the trails, he'd more easily receive the alien voices. They were giving him some great material for the children's books he still intended on writing after the pandemic.

Billy met a lot of people living mostly on the street. He liked the camaraderie. He also discovered methamphetamines and crack helped his creativity. Cocaine helped in the past but was expensive and not nearly as good.

He drafted story ideas in a notebook he found in the trash. He found a hat in a used clothing store that almost perfectly resembled the hat worn by Willy Wonka. It had magical properties. When he wore it, his creative juices flowed, and he wrote furiously. If you happened to glimpse what he was writing, it'd appear to be gibberish. To him? It made perfect sense.

Not wanting other kids to have to endure what he went through; Billy had a plan. He would make their dreams come true.

The marijuana mellowed him, but methamphetamines helped him stay up for days.

He saw violent protests, looting, and innocent people getting killed. People arrested for major crimes were getting let out with little or no bail right back on the streets. It gave him ideas.

Billy started small by taking things like chips and sodas and walking out the door of convenience stores because he knew he could. The shop owners knew if they called the police, nothing would be done, so they just let it happen to keep the peace.

When he broke into a store by breaking the glass, the alarm went off. The local police knew Billy was a homeless dealer, but they never bothered him. The new District Attorney wasn't prosecuting small crimes.

Billy was arrested for breaking and entering, but only spent a brief time in jail since it was his first offense.

He was evaluated by the psychiatrist at the prison and was diagnosed with paranoid schizophrenia due to his history and symptoms. The doctor surmised his drug use worsened the situation. He had a significant family history, with an alcoholic, drug addict, and bipolar father. Billy's grandmother suffered chronic mental illness and ended up in a mental institution. She was prescribed electroconvulsive therapy. His mother also harbored mental illness on her side of the family, which she wouldn't speak of.

The doctor surmised the family history, persistent drug use, and traumatic upbringing contributed to Billy's mental state. He was deemed not a threat, but was warned if he were arrested again, it'd lead to more extensive jail time.

Billy didn't want to go back. It was too crowded, the other prisoners scared him, and he didn't have easy access to drugs like on the street.

Trying tiny amounts of fentanyl that'd been smuggled in, prisoners told him how much to take and to be careful. He liked the opiates he had tried in the past, but they weren't as good. He made a deal with certain prisoners he'd sell them marijuana at a reduced rate when he got out if he could get fentanyl from them since he didn't feel comfortable dealing it himself.

Billy was on his best behavior when he got out since he did not want to ever go back. He liked the feeling of being free, only occasionally going back to where he used to live. The room at his friend's house was often not available, so he'd just take the belongings he needed with him. Billy actually preferred that lifestyle.

As the year 2020 ended and 2021 began, he noticed people still wore masks. "I didn't understand why."

He knew other street people who never wore masks, "… and they weren't dying of this supposedly deadly virus. It just didn't make sense since most of the media outlets said otherwise. Plenty of people died of overdoses, though, because they weren't careful and knowledgeable like me."

When the vaccines came out Billy became suspicious. He already didn't trust the government, and since he had a lot of free time, he was able to do his own research. He learned they were experimental vaccines created with recent technology that'd not been adequately tested. No human trials and no data supported their safety. "They weren't FDA approved yet were being pushed on the general population. I read about it on a laptop I'd charge at my friend's house or wherever."

He looked at the CDC's own VAERS (Vaccine Adverse Events Reporting System) site where they admitted to several thousand deaths and permanent injuries from their use. Billy's research revealed it was likely a significant undercount. He wanted to save humanity, so he tried spreading the word to anybody that'd listen and not fall for their tactics and not get their vaccines under any circumstances. He warned people to not listen to that old man appearing often on TV.

He was so happy when the aliens came back. Billy heard them most clearly after taking methamphetamines or crack. He accessed his higher power, who interpreted what the aliens said to him. They made it clear the virus was released on purpose, and the vaccines were weapons that were going to be used to control people and kill as many as possible.

When he saw the movie, *Died Suddenly* it confirmed his suspicions. More than a million people in the United States died from the supposedly safe vaccines. He told everyone he could to watch it and judge for themselves.

Some of his friends called him paranoid and others labelled him a conspiracy theorist and radical. They didn't understand his special connection to higher powers that revealed the truth to him. He was able to look up information from credible scientists that were typically censored, confirming his suspicions that something was just not right. He saw mass hysteria and fear unlike any he or many others had ever experienced.

Social media and conservative news outlets were censored and ignored. Most people just didn't know the truth.

He became irate learning they were pushing vaccines on kids who are at zero risk of dying from the virus. He feared it would cost many more lives than it'd save. There was risk of permanent injury for many. Billy needed to protect the kids.

He was Willy Wonka, and he would save all the children and make all their dreams come true.

Billy warned people he met on the street about the vaccines and the propaganda. Some were tempted with offers of free food, free drinks or a free joint if they agreed to get the vaccine. The government was desperate to poison as much of society as possible. It was Billy's responsibility to stop them.

He was ecstatic with the news he and others had been right. The people accused of being "conspiracy theorists" and "radical right-wingers" were correct all along. There was so much conflict, and he knew so many people died unnecessarily. Even though he was upset, he knew the wrongdoers would be exposed.

His message of hope was needed more than ever. He could save children. He could fulfill their dreams, which drove him to writing. Most of his time was spent imagining and fantasizing, while not getting most of it on paper. This didn't stop him, though, since he knew he was creating at a higher level than any other person had ever been. Billy possessed special powers installed by the aliens that had worked within him to fulfill their vision.

He used methamphetamines more and the words flowed. The pen produced nonsensical words and symbols. After all of the multiple hours writing he couldn't put together one children's book because he had too many ideas and too much information to narrow down to such a small piece of work.

After being up for several days, Billy needed sleep. He found marijuana would relax him, but opiates would relax him more. He'd occasionally get pain pills such as Oxycontin or Percocet on the street and chop them up and do lines. This helped his brain relax after the excessive amount of writing and going all over to warn people against the vaccine and the lying public health officials.

After a day of drug-induced sleeping, he'd get back on meth or crack in order to write his important work for hours, with little to show for it. The aliens understood his purpose and trusted him with the information they provided.

He'd contact his mother when he had access to a phone to tell her he was okay. "I have important work I'm doing and I'm going to save lots of people including you. Be careful and don't listen to the news. Don't follow any government instructions."

"I'm nervous about what I'm hearing," she said, "and I'm worried about you."

"I've never been better," he reassured her, "and my thoughts are clearer than ever."

After Billy hung up, his mom was concerned. "It just didn't sound like him anymore."

After he rested after being up for so many days, he knew he had too much to do and should not be sleeping. After several additional sleepless nights due to methamphetamine use, he bought an opiate pill on the street and was told it was a strong pain pill. He hadn't seen one that looked like that before but knew it'd give him some rest so he could get back to his writing and creating.

He took it and soon felt extremely relaxed and peaceful and laid down to rest.

Billy hadn't felt so relaxed for quite some time. What he didn't realize was 25% of the street drugs, including Xanax, Klonopin and other tranquilizers, cocaine, ADD medications, and pain pills of various types were laced with fentanyl, which had proven to be fatal in low doses.

Billy had taken it before in prison and believed he knew how much was safe. He had lost some friends to opiate overdoses including fentanyl, but knew he'd be fine because he was too smart to let that happen.

He'd never injected drugs and wouldn't take things that far. He vowed against heroin because of what he'd heard. Fentanyl was better, anyway. He took tiny amounts and knew how much was safe. This was just an opiate pill, though, which he had a lot of experience with. He knew it was harmless. Or so he thought.

Billy dreamt vividly. Greeted by a spaceship, some of the female aliens looked like girls he was attracted to in high school. They were so friendly and inviting and welcomed him into their spaceship. They said his mission was complete and praised him for his hard work. He'd made a significant difference and saved many people, making many children's wishes and dreams come true.

He dreamt about that moment for so long. He was finally going to travel into space to another planet, fulfilling his destiny and completing his mission. He wouldn't miss the Earth since he was going on a new adventure to a much better place.

The next morning, when his cold body was found with his arms outstretched, he wore a broad smile across his face.

CHAPTER 16

School Shootings

A school shooting is an attack involving the use of firearms at an educational institution, such as primary school, secondary school, or university. This phenomenon is most widespread in the United States. It's common in other countries, as well. Factors contributing to school shootings include family dysfunction, the lack of supervision, easy access to firearms, mental illness, drug use, addiction also factor in. Psychological, psychiatric, and medical factors also contribute, making this issue complex and difficult to resolve.

The top motives of perpetrators are bullying, persecution, being threatened, seeking attention or recognition, suicidal thoughts, and trying to solve a problem.

Typical characteristics describing shooters are that they're middle-class, lonely, alienated, awkward, Caucasian males with access to guns. Authorities warn that's not always the case as there's a lot of variety among perpetrators. The majority have never gotten into trouble at school or in their personal lives.

Family stability, as well as the presence of two parents, including a father or father figure, decreases the chance a boy will become a shooter. The actual family makeup isn't as important as their stability.

Studies found that within an offender's family, there's a frequent lack of supervision, low emotional bonding, and lack of an intimate connection.

They tend to isolate and exhibit an obsessive-compulsive desire to make detailed plans of the attack. They lack an understanding of the consequences of their behaviors, and thus may not have a history of adverse encounters with law enforcement.

They may leave clues others might notice in order to avert tragedies, but their horror can be difficult to stop. They do not understand the difference between right and wrong, good and evil. It's difficult to understand the corrupt, sick mind of a criminal, especially a killer. The rational and healthy mind just can't comprehend how another individual can carry out such atrocities.

Data shows the weapon is likely taken from their home or from a relative. The availability of firearms has a direct effect on the probability of initiating a school shooting.

Some advocate for parents to be held criminally responsible if their firearm is used in an attack, which is controversial. Most agree the owner of a firearm should store it carefully and securely so the weapon doesn't fall into the wrong hands.

The shooter's family usually has few or no limits, and the shooter insists on an inordinate degree of privacy. Parents have little information about their activities, school life or friends.

Some parents feel intimidated by their child's violent tendencies when attempting discipline. Parents and caretakers try to avoid temper tantrums and meltdowns, so they end up being controlled. They don't set limits for free time, such as limiting video games, their type, social media, and internet. It's set up for risky behaviors, especially if the child spends a disproportionate amount of time exposed to inappropriate and dangerous material that can indoctrinate them. These influences can be suitably balanced with other aspects of their lives.

Shooters spend a lot of time playing and watching violent video games, violent movies and TV shows. It's controversial how much of a role violent video games play, but to me, it makes common sense that spending so much time with them desensitizes kids and numbs their emotions. The majority of players would never consider doing such things. Parents are often blamed for such outcomes but even if the parents do a fantastic job of parenting, these events still happen.

In most cases, a significant risk factor for developing school shooters is poor parenting. Children need to learn life lessons and the difference between right and wrong from their caretakers, the ones who are supposed to love and care for them. If their children do not learn the basic life lessons and skills, it can lead to bad outcomes, sometimes dangerous and fatal.

Immaturity is one of the many identifying factors that increase the likelihood of an individual conducting acts of violence. A critical issue is whether the child is satisfied with and has the patience for delayed gratification instead of the temptation of giving in to instant gratification. Herein lies the likelihood of immaturity and impulsive acts.

To understand the difference between instant gratification and delayed gratification I recommend you look at the research behind the Marshmallow test.

A large marshmallow is placed in front of a child and he or she is told that if they wait and not eat it for a certain amount of time until the researcher comes back. They'll get an extra one, totaling two. If it is eaten before the researcher comes back, the one marshmallow is all they get. Observed behind one-way glass, the child makes a difficult decision. The videos are fun to watch as they struggle with their choice.

The differences between the two groups are astonishing. The delayed gratification kids did better socially, academically, as well as career stability and overall life.

Most instant gratification-oriented kids performed poorly in all of these aspects. This study underscores the significance of parents setting boundaries for their children, imparting the values of earning rewards rather than expecting something for nothing. For instance, if a child misbehaves because a parent denies their request, the parent should use it as an opportunity to teach the child the importance of displaying better behavior and earning favors. The adage "Patience is a Virtue" is applicable in this context.

Bullying, a pervasive issue in schools, appears to play a pivotal role in the lives of many school shooters. The typical bullying scenario involves three key roles: the offender or bully, the victim, and one or more bystanders. This formula is advantageous for bullies as it allows them to publicly humiliate their victims. Students who experience bullying often develop behavioral problems, depression, low self-esteem, anxiety, and other mood disorders. Individuals with a predisposition for criminal behavior typically show poor self-control and social skills.

Media sensationalism may contribute to the shooter's desire to create a larger impact. Perpetrators who are captured alive often cite the desire to be remembered as a primary motivation for their planned shootings.

There are also individuals known as "injustice collectors" who never forget, never forgive, and never let go. They share a common trait of lacking remorse, indicative of sociopathic tendencies. These individuals, in essence, lack a moral compass and are among the most unsettling and dangerous individuals one can encounter.

The role of mental illness in school shootings has been a topic of debate. However, it seems evident that school shooters and mass murderers are severely mentally ill. The acts they commit are cold-blooded, and it is difficult to argue that they do not exhibit signs of mental illness.

Most often, school shooters remain undiagnosed, untreated, misdiagnosed, mistreated, or a combination of these. They often grapple with psychiatric illnesses such as bipolar disorder, marked by manic flare-ups and severe depressive cycles, as well as schizophrenia, anxiety or depressive disorders, and post-traumatic stress disorder (PTSD) stemming from various traumas, or a combination thereof. Additionally, they often show at least one personality disorder, most commonly antisocial personality disorder, but also possibly narcissistic, borderline, paranoid, schizoid, schizotypal, or others. When multiple personality disorders coexist, the outcome can be deadly.

School shooters are complex individuals who desperately require the attention and treatment that is frequently lacking. This should encompass medical professionals knowledgeable about the use of psychotropic medications and extensive psychological support. Unfortunately, these needs often go unaddressed, leading untreated individuals down a dangerous and potentially lethal path.

The use of drugs among school shooters varies. Some are heavily involved in substance abuse, while others are risk-takers perpetually seeking new thrills and highs. Among the drugs mentioned, the most dangerous are those in the amphetamine class, such as methamphetamines, crack cocaine, and cocaine, as well as other street stimulants, including prescription medications intended for those with ADD/ADHD. These drugs can induce mania and acute psychosis.

Substance abuse, particularly of stimulants, has the potential to cause permanent brain damage and complicate treatment due to synaptic burnout, making it less responsive to medication. Potent modern forms of marijuana, hallucinogens, and other potent street drugs may also play a role. Giving an antidepressant to one with bipolar disorder can drive a person into mania, which can increase risk.

Individuals with antisocial personality tendencies are unlikely to respond to counseling, especially if they do not acknowledge themselves as a problem. Their best hope lies in a spiritual conversion to steer them from wrong to right, immoral to moral, and evil to good.

Keith

From an early age, Keith struggled to form close connections with others. His mother's neglect, heightened by her involvement in substance abuse and fleeting relationships with numerous men, disrupted the critical mother-child bond during his early years. She rarely held, nurtured, or comforted him, leaving Keith to fend for himself when he sought attention, sustenance, or care.

Keith had occasional encounters with his father, but these were far from pleasant. Many of his childhood memories were tainted by the physical and emotional abuse he endured at the hands of his father. This abuse culminated in his father's conviction for domestic violence when he assaulted his wife and she dialed 911. Keith also recalled his father's intermittent stints in prison, resulting from various criminal activities he was involved in.

For most of his childhood and adolescence, Keith's father remained absent from his life, a situation he was content with. He also made efforts to distance himself from his mother.

During his elementary school years, Keith had a few sporadic friendships but preferred solitude, often isolating himself. He was of slight build and had no interest in sports, a fact his parents showed little concern about when the school tried to intervene. Their apathy led the school to abandon the matter, which Keith considered a significant victory.

Keith endured relentless teasing and taunting due to his small stature. He was often referred to as a "midget" or a "runt" and ridiculed for his social awkwardness and shyness. To escape the torment, he sought refuge in secluded areas at school between classes and after school.

At home, Keith isolated himself by locking his bedroom door with a two-way lock to safeguard his privacy and shield himself from any remarks about the chaotic state of his room. He kept his window locked from the inside to prevent intrusion. His forays into the kitchen for food were brief, after which he'd retreat to his sanctuary. He spent countless hours engrossed in violent video games and indulged in gruesome horror TV shows and movies.

Keith liked being outside and enjoying fresh air, even if it meant smoking a joint to help him grapple with his thoughts. He couldn't believe he was entertaining such ideas and whimsical notions, but there was another part of him that darkly indulged the festering thoughts.

Keith knew how to manipulate his mother, convincing her to buy the latest and most explicit video games, well aware that he wasn't supposed to have them at his age. His mother, fearing his potential outbursts and the resemblance to his father, reluctantly agreed to sign for them as long as he promised not to react negatively if she ever said no.

At school, Keith observed the various social cliques, such as the jocks, popular kids, cheerleader followers, the academically inclined, nerds/geeks, pretenders, drama and music enthusiasts, and club members—groups he actively avoided.

He had no desire to be part of any of these cliques, evading all school activities and doing the bare minimum, such as attending classes and slipping away before anyone could approach him. Upon dismissal, he made a swift return home to his safe haven, his room. He collected enough fast food, using money either given by his mother or taken from her, to minimize his contact with the kitchen. Although dark thoughts lingered, he tried to suppress them, at least for a time.

In middle school, Keith noticed his peers undergoing significant physical and emotional changes. His own transformation was not as pronounced, leaving him feeling out of place. He saw shifts in their attitudes, seeing increased aggression and relentless teasing about his appearance, with peers using derogatory terms like "wimp" and "pussy" and questioning his sexuality. The teachers appeared indifferent, as did his peers, but Keith was equally disinterested in them.

In the solace of his room, Keith immersed himself in violent video games for hours on end. He began to project the faces of those he despised at school onto the characters he virtually dispatched. He ventured into alternate worlds and fantasies, occasionally enhancing the experience with substances like shrooms and marijuana. His virtual adventures became increasingly centered on brutal violence, and his thoughts took a disturbing turn.

* * *

During the second week of his sophomore year, things got worse. Some of the jocks/jerks were continuing to make fun of his size and called him a "faggot." He tried ignoring their comments, but sometimes they pushed him and punched him in the arm as they laughed at him. His so-called "friends" just stood silently and did nothing. Sometimes they seemed to encourage it by smiling and laughing. They were never really friends, anyway, judging by how they acted when he needed them. Everyone let him down; he could only count on himself.

The cheerleader types ignored him. They looked down on him and would never be interested in someone like him. He had fantasies about being with them, though he knew it was impossible. They were just stuck-up bitches, so full of themselves. He knew they hung out with the jocks most of the time. They made fun of his bad grades and called him "stupid," "moron," "weirdo" and a "freak," and then laughed at him.

He noticed the teachers didn't intervene when he was being teased and taunted. In fact, teachers picked on him by calling on him when they knew that he didn't know the answer. He didn't want them to expose him. The other kids would laugh when he'd stare blankly at the teacher and did not understand the question, much less the answer. Even the teacher seemed a bit amused.

He didn't feel important to anybody. He just didn't matter and was angry. Keith considered fulfilling his fantasy. They would learn to respect him. He would make them. He couldn't bear the thought of three more years in the place. He had to act.

Keith had been hatching a plan for quite a while. He would make sure he'd be noticed, feared, and respected. He'd be famous.

Though he was definitely not close to his father growing up, he'd listened and learned a lot about guns from him. They'd go target shooting. He taught his son how to properly handle a firearm by taking it apart and storing it and then how to put it back together. His father was impressed by Keith's shooting abilities during target practice with little previous experience, other than video games. Keith was not used to being praised by one of his parents.

His father also had several old "collector" guns. There was a couple he kept at his mother's house, and his father had taught her and him how to use them in order to protect them in case someone broke in. Keith knew exactly how to make them work.

The next morning, he took a couple of rifles and a handgun and hid them under his jacket and went to school. The other students arrived, expecting a typical day.

He was past the point of despair and anguish. He internalized his anger and resentment. He wanted as many people as possible to pay for their transgressions and for them to beg for mercy as he decided who'd live and die. For Keith it was the ultimate justice, and he'd enjoy every moment.

Keith planned it out carefully. There were four jocks and three of the stuck-up cheerleader types in the first classroom. He knew who were in the next two classrooms and how he'd go about methodically killing them. He'd gone over his game plan many times. There was only one shot.

He barged into the first classroom and shot three of the guys and two of the girls before they knew what hit them. He hit one guy right in the middle of the chest, leaving a gaping hole with blood gushing out. The other guy tried to hide but Keith went over and took care of him as he begged for mercy. He saved the best for last: the girl he desired and hated the most. He shot that bitch in the middle of her face, splattering blood all over her fake blonde hair. What a perfect shot.

It was going according to plan. He needed to get into the next room before anyone realized what was happening. He imagined their faces like video game characters, only it was happening in real life instead of his fantasies.

He slipped out as the students ran from the classroom and down the hallway, slipping on blood.

Keith arrived in the second classroom just in time. When he opened the door, they looked surprised. He took out three planned targets, including one of his so-called "friends" that never stuck up for him. Everyone was screaming and running towards the door or were hiding and whimpering under their desks.

He barreled into the third classroom where the teacher he hated the most stood. The teacher looked surprised with his mouth open when Keith shot him in the middle of his head, splattering pieces of his brain, gore, and blood all over the floor. His lifeless body toppled. Keith searched for other targets on his list but couldn't find them all in the pandemonium. It was okay. He could always come back and finish the job another time. There were still plenty of targets to take out. He needn't be so greedy. He needed to be patient and enjoy the moment.

Kids screamed and cried as they rushed out the door.

He figured out the best escape plan was going out the back entrance, the way he normally slipped out when the school day ended in order to get home before the other kids and teachers left.

They normally went out the front door so he figured they would go out the same way, which meant his best option was to go the other way. However, because of the utter chaos, the kids and teachers were going as quickly as possible through each door, so he tried to hide inside the crowd as they left the building.

Other than slipping out the back and escaping, he didn't have a backup plan. He packed up what he needed, since he'd be identified, and the cops would investigate his place soon enough. He'd try to change his identity and live as he'd always wanted to, like John Wick, Dexter Morgan, or other characters he admired.

He looked forward to fleeing life and existing alone. It sounded like heaven. He'd stolen enough money from his parents to get by for a while. He'd have to steal more at some point and get an alias, maybe grow a beard, wear a hat and sunglasses, whatever it would take to blend in. He would be able to read news accounts about his exploits. Since his whereabouts would be unknown, he would be feared. He would finally get the respect he deserved.

Of course, he'd thought about what'd happen if he didn't escape, though he was so sure he would. Time in prison didn't bother him. He would have plenty of time alone, have a bed and be fed regularly. Didn't sound so bad. The other prisoners would stay away from him because they'd fear him for what he'd done.

Keith chastised himself for thinking so negatively since he was most likely going to be able to escape. He had big plans ahead of him. He would stick to the wilderness and find a place where no one would find him. Maybe he 'd find a cave somewhere and live off the land and hunt for prey. He just proved how good he was at hunting.

He would have to go into town occasionally of course in order to get staples like fast food, groceries and whatever would make living off the land easier.

Keith knew that his face would be all over the news, and they'd be looking for him. He would need to cover his face as much as possible. It was the perfect timing for this because due to the pandemic so many people were wearing masks. He thought that they looked stupid, but the timing couldn't be better for him. Maybe he would go to an underground plastic surgeon that would alter his appearance since he had read about facial recognition that was being used to look for criminals.

As he moved out of the back entrance trying to blend in with the crowd many of the students and teachers were separating from him and pointing to him, which is when he heard the sirens blaring. They screamed at the police officers that the person they were pointing to was the perpetrator. He whipped his head around when he heard the police telling him to drop his weapons and put his hands up. This didn't look good.

Keith was confronted with a tricky situation. He could try to shoot his way out and take as many targets as possible, but the probability was that he would be struck and killed. What kind of a stupid idea was that? That would just prove that he was weak and unable to take it. It would just waste what he had done since he would not be alive to enjoy his accomplishment. They would win and he would lose, and he couldn't let that happen.

Keith couldn't believe he thought about shooting himself in the head if he got cornered. What a stupid idea. How could he be feared if he was dead?

He realized his escape plans weren't working out and it was coming to an end. Was he really losing, though? Sure, he wanted to escape but this way would also work out well for him, too. He'd be able to get the peace he needed and the recognition and fame he deserved.

Keith threw his arms dramatically above his head while throwing both rifles and the handgun as far as he could. He went down to his knees and stretched his arms out while lying face down on the ground.

The police reported they got creeped out when they detained him. He wore a wide smile plastered across his face.

CHAPTER 17

Suicide

Suicide is the act of intentionally causing one's own death. Mental illness is a major contributing factor, including conditions such as depression, anxiety disorders, obsessive-compulsive disorder, bipolar disorder, autistic spectrum disorders, schizophrenia, personality disorders, and others, often in combination, making them some of the most challenging cases to address. While there is an ongoing debate about the percentage of suicide cases linked to mental illness, it's widely recognized that mental health plays a significant role.

Bipolar disorder, for instance, increases the risk of suicide twentyfold. Other contributing factors include chronic pain, physical disorders, chronic fatigue syndrome, substance abuse, and withdrawal. Substance abuse is closely intertwined with mental illness, and often one doesn't occur without the other. Personality disorders, particularly borderline personality disorder, are also linked to an increased risk of suicide. In many cases, a combination of these conditions contributes to the desperate act of taking one's own life.

Some suicides are impulsive acts triggered by stress, which can be either acute or chronic. Stressors may include financial difficulties, job loss, academic challenges, relationship breakups, divorces, harassment, bullying, physical or sexual abuse, poverty, unemployment, homelessness, and traumatic brain injury. Chronic and painful conditions, cancer diagnoses, and a bleak outlook on life can also contribute to suicidal thoughts. Suicide risk is significantly higher among veterans suffering from PTSD.

A history of earlier suicide attempts, genetic predisposition, and easy access to suicide methods, such as firearms, prescription drugs, street drugs, poisons, and other means, further increase the risk. The most common methods of suicide vary by country and are partly related to the availability of effective means. Common methods include hanging, firearms, intentional overdoses, and poisons.

In the United States, suicide is ranked as the 10th most common cause of death, claiming around 1 million lives annually, which accounts for approximately 1.5% of all deaths worldwide. In some countries, such as China, suicide is the leading cause of death, with a particularly high rate among females. Suicidal rates are often higher in communist countries and places with limited individual rights, such as Russia, Cuba, and Venezuela. North Korea, plagued by severe poverty and starvation, has seen a soaring suicide rate, sometimes involving entire families.

High female suicide rates are also seen in South Korea, Southeast Asia, and the Western Pacific. Overall, completed suicides are more common among men than women, with rates ranging from 1.5 times more likely in the developing world to 3.5 times more likely in the developed world. Men tend to choose more violent means, such as shooting and hanging, which are often fatal. Women are more likely to try overdoses, some of which are thankfully unsuccessful, providing an opportunity for intervention.

While suicide is most common among those over the age of 70, in certain countries, individuals between 15 and 30 are at the highest risk. There are an estimated 10 to 20 million nonfatal suicide attempts each year, which can lead to injuries and long-term disabilities in some cases. In the Western world, suicide attempts are more common among young people, particularly young females.

Views on suicide have been influenced by various existential themes, including religion, honor, and the meaning of life. Many traditional Judeo-Christian religions consider suicide an offense against God due to the belief in the sanctity of life. Some countries still consider suicide a criminal offense.

The impact of suicide is devastating for families, relatives, and friends. It often leaves survivors burdened with guilt, wondering what they could have done differently to prevent it. The pain and guilt may persist for many years, if not a lifetime. Suicide is viewed negatively almost everywhere around the world, causing profound human tragedies for those left behind.

Now, let's break down suicide into different contributing factors, starting with psychosocial factors. These encompass personality traits like neuroticism and being introverted, which may lead to isolation and despair. Some common signs of suicidality include hopelessness, loss of interest in once-enjoyable activities (anhedonia), depressed mood, anxiety, agitation, rumination, obsessive and rigid thinking, and others. Poor coping skills, problem-solving abilities, and impulse control issues also increase the risk of suicide.

In older adults, feeling like a burden to others, losing a family member or close friend, social isolation, and a lack of support are additional risk factors. Poverty, especially in comparison to those around them, and substantial debt can elevate the risk. The time of year may affect suicide rates, with decreases around Christmas and increases during spring and summer. Being religious may reduce one's overall risk, though this is a subject of debate.

Substance abuse is the second most common risk factor after bipolar disorder and major depressive disorder. Acute intoxication, often related to chronic substance abuse, can heighten the risk of suicide. People at risk are often under the influence of sedative-hypnotic drugs, such as alcohol and benzodiazepines, when they take their own lives. Opiates, like pain pills and heroin, are common substances associated with suicide, sometimes unintentionally due to overdose. Cocaine and methamphetamines also have a strong correlation with suicide, with the highest risk during the withdrawal phase in cocaine users. Inhalant use and cigarette smoking are linked to increased suicide risk as well.

Physical health problems, such as chronic pain conditions, traumatic brain injury, cancer, chronic fatigue syndrome, kidney failure requiring hemodialysis, HIV, systemic lupus erythematosus, and chronic recurring illnesses, are also associated with higher suicide risk. Sleep disturbances, including insomnia and sleep apnea, can be risk factors for depression and suicide. Certain medical conditions can present symptoms resembling mood disorders. Some medications, like beta blockers and steroids, may slightly increase the risk. The media and the Internet play a significant role in suicide. Depictions of suicide can influence its occurrence, especially when they romanticize or supply detailed descriptions of specific methods, potentially leading to "copycat suicides."

Suicide attacks are political or religious actions in which the attacker carries out violence against others, knowing it will result in their own death. Suicide bombers, often radical Islamists, are motivated by hatred of their enemies and the desire to reach martyrdom. Kamikaze pilots in World War II adopted a similar approach, aiming to maximize the harm to the enemy. Some inmates in Nazi concentration camps deliberately touched electrified fences to end their lives. Murder-suicide refers to a murder followed within a week by the suicide of the perpetrator, although it typically happens immediately after the murder.

The choice of suicide method varies by country, influenced by the availability of different means. Common methods include hanging, pesticide poisoning, and firearms. Hanging is statistically the most common method in many countries, especially in the developed world, accounting for approximately 53% of male suicides and 39% of female suicides. Drug overdoses account for around 60% of suicides among women and 30% among men in various countries, while death by firearms is more common in the United States due to easy access. Many suicides are impulsive, occurring after a brief period of ambivalence. Other methods include carbon monoxide poisoning, jumping, drowning, and charcoal burning. In China, pesticide poisoning is the most frequent method, while drug overdoses are common in the developed world. Firearms, particularly in Switzerland, are also prevalent methods, especially among males.

Suicide prevention, often referred to as suicide prevention efforts, is crucial for addressing the issue of suicide through preventive measures. These measures include providing support from family and friends, as well as support groups. Ready access to therapy and counseling is also essential, as more than half of people with suicidal thoughts do not seek help, often due to several reasons, including stigma, fear of medications, and the desire to handle it alone. Additionally, reducing access to lethal methods like firearms, toxins, and certain medications can make impulsive attempts less likely to succeed. Barriers on bridges and subway platforms can also help reduce suicide risks.

Treatment of drug and alcohol addiction, as well as bipolar disorder, depression, or other mental health diagnoses, significantly decreases the risk of suicide. Suicide hotlines provide valuable support, offering individuals someone to talk to when they need it most. Those with a history of suicide attempts are at the highest risk and should be closely monitored. The Internet can both pose a risk by promoting harmful information and offer support through communication with others.

In young adults with recent suicidal thoughts, cognitive-behavioral therapy has been shown to improve outcomes. School-based programs that increase mental health awareness can identify at-risk individuals. Self-harming behaviors are fairly common among teenagers, especially girls, and can serve as a clear cry for help. Addressing childhood trauma is essential for preventing suicidal tendencies.

Efforts to increase social connection, particularly among elderly males, may be effective in reducing suicide rates. Providers should inquire about suicidal ideation, especially among unstable patients. If patients have a plan, this constitutes a true emergency, requiring immediate intervention. For those with ideation but no concrete plan, a suicide contract may be documented, and verbal contracts have shown to be effective. Clear documentation is essential for treating providers. Short-term psychiatric hospitalization may be necessary when situations are acute.

Borderline personality disorder is a risk factor for chronic recurring suicidal ideation, typically emerging in teenage years and young adulthood. Dialectical behavioral therapy (DBT) is the most effective psychotherapy for these patients.

There is some confusion about the increased risk of suicidality in teenagers and young adults using antidepressants. This confusion may stem from the fact that antidepressants can increase the risk in individuals with bipolar disorder if they trigger mania or worsen depression. However, antidepressants significantly reduce the risk for those with unipolar depression and anxiety disorders. For bipolar patients who are unstable, starting with a mood stabilizer is often the best approach, with antidepressants introduced when the patient is more stable.

Genetics plays a significant role in completed suicides. A family history of suicide, especially in the mother, affects children more than adolescents or adults. Adoption studies have proven that biological relatives, rather than adopted ones, are more prone to suicide. Genetic predisposition is a crucial element in mental illness, and individuals often inherit the majority of their genetic load from the parent or relatives they most resemble, both physically and emotionally.

Legislation varies around the world. Suicide is not considered a crime in most European countries, unlike in the past when it was illegal. Assisted suicide is legalized in certain countries, but strict protocols are followed. In the United States, suicide attempts are not technically illegal, but penalties may be associated with them. Physician-assisted suicide is legal in some states, such as Washington and Oregon, under specific conditions. In Canada, physician-assisted suicide has seen a significant increase. Legislation on suicide varies widely in Muslim-majority countries, where it is often illegal.

Veronica

Veronica just wanted to be loved. She craved attention from her father who was cold and distant. "I can't remember a time when he hugged me or told me he loved me. He and my mom would yell and scream at each other, though he didn't usually physically harm her. I was an only child, since my mother couldn't carry another pregnancy, which was one of the things my dad was upset about. He'd put her down about that and pretty much everything. We lived in a good neighborhood, and I was well provided for and was not in want of anything, except love and affection." Which was what she wanted more than anything.

Towards the end of elementary school, Veronica got attention from boys, which seemed to correlate with significant changes in her body. Later in life, her therapist told her it was the beginning of when getting the attention from men took the place of what she didn't receive from her father. Regardless? It was exciting to be noticed by so many boys.

The relationships always started exciting, but that changed when they lost interest, or she got bored.

During these years, her moods changed, too, from depression and then anxiety, or both. She had mood swings a week prior to her menstruation. Veronica was crying for no apparent reason. Petty things irritated her.

When guys saw her dark side, they'd leave the relationship, which made Veronica more and more desperate each time it happened. She spoke to a school counselor, but her parents didn't try to get help.

In high school she was introduced to drinking, marijuana and occasionally cocaine, but in college her drinking and drug use escalated. "Free from my parents and living away from home, I relished the experience and celebrated quite frequently," she said.

Veronica did well enough in school as a Communications major, which led later to a job in sales. However, she did better at partying and experiencing as much of the social scene as she could. This included relationships which were like a revolving door. She had some girlfriends she'd hang out with, but most of her friendships were with guys.

She loved the beginnings of relationships but got bored or the guy wouldn't put up with her excessive drinking, drugs, and erratic moods. "I had suicidal thoughts when things were at their worst, but I decided not to act on them."

There were times she was in serious danger when abusing drugs and alcohol. She discovered Xanax, Klonopin and other benzodiazepines. Sometimes she'd mix one or more with cocaine and alcohol, which would produce high-highs and low-lows. Veronica learned how to minimize the lows and maximize the highs.

After college she got a corporate sales job after dazzling the interviewers with her looks and charm. She liked the fact that it was a male-dominated industry since she felt that she fit right in. She would have brief affairs with men in the office, though she focused her efforts on corporate types that'd climbed up the ladder.

She learned to control her temper in her 20s, or at least how to hide it better. She continued to self-medicate and could hide it well … at least she thought she could.

At a conference she met a man, Jack, who worked at a different company doing similar work. They hit it off right away. She loved the start of relationships when she'd first meet a guy and experience strong feelings.

"The initial excitement did not wear off," she said. "Even though there were some rocky times in our dating relationship, which seemed to happen when I drank too much, we always made up and moved on."

They got married in their late 20s, despite concerns from his family.

"Withing four years we had a girl and then a boy, and I was happy," Veronica said. "I still suffered with mood swings and depression after the first pregnancy but then it got worse after the second." She was given an antidepressant after the first one, but she only felt slightly better. A second medicine taken after the following pregnancy produced a much worse reaction. "My moods actually got worse, and I had suicidal ideation. Jack was concerned but felt that there was nothing he could do to help me feel better."

Jack avoided Veronica when her frequent temper flares; he'd get verbally and physically assaulted. He'd try to restrain her but not strike back, which made matters worse.

Several months after their second pregnancy, Veronica seemed less erratic and doing better. Unfortunately, she was still far from stable.

Veronica enjoyed being involved with her kids' activities, and she liked quitting work and raising the kids full-time. They were involved in different sports, and she was involved in each sport they took part in. She had difficulty getting along with the other mothers, however, she seemed to enjoy being around their husbands. She noticed she'd not get invited to some of the activities with the other women.

"They were jealous because their husbands were more interested in me than them," she said. "And Jack was jealous when I talked to the other husbands, too, which was great."

Her reoccurring and erratic pattern continued for the next decade, along with her abuse of alcohol and prescription drugs.

Jack had enough and informed her he wanted to divorce. "I was frantic and begged for him to go to marriage counseling with me. We tried but it didn't work."

Her moods became more erratic; the psychologist recommended individual counseling, but recognized it wasn't enough and thus referred her to a doctor that specialized in mental health.

Veronica was in her early 40s and, thankfully, the doctor recognized what was happening and how to treat it. Her primary care doctor had tried her on a couple different antidepressants with mixed results. Within the next 2 months, she was started on an antidepressant followed by a mood stabilizer, and then another antidepressant. Topamax was then added as the final piece, which helped to control her binge drinking and eating as well as her residual anxiety.

"I never felt better in my life," she said. "The doctor told me I had bipolar two disorder. With the combination of depression and hypomania, it can lead to dramatic mood swings if not treated and maintained effectively."

She felt so much better, though, she didn't feel the need to self-medicate with alcohol and other drugs. She could control the drinking, though that wasn't the case once she started.

Veronica struggled with accepting the divorce but knew she couldn't save the marriage. She needed to move on.

Shaking it off, she realized, "I was good at moving on. I'd been bored being married, anyway. Time for a new relationship."

Over the following years, when she felt good in a new relationship, she didn't think she needed to keep taking the medications, so she'd stop them. She'd follow up with the doctor only when she was desperate and needed to be talked into going back on the combination that worked for her.

Each time she restarted the medications, she felt good. After a period, she'd decide to stop and would feel okay for a short time, but it didn't last. She said, "I didn't want to be on so many medications and questioned if I even had bipolar."

Her doctor was adamant the best way to treat her condition was the correct combination of psychotropic medications. The doctor pointed out she'd have not had such good results with the combination if the diagnosis was not correct.

She was having problems communicating with her ex-husband and argued about child custody. They agreed to split 50-50, and both lived close.

Her kids wanted to spend as little time with her as possible. Her daughter was tired of the drama and verbal altercations, and her son evaded her. The kids were at the ages where they had some leeway in deciding who to spend their time with.

There was a rough incident with her daughter. During an intense argument, Veronica took most of a bottle of Xanax in front of her daughter. Her daughter called her father, who called 911 and took her to the hospital. They pumped her stomach and observed her for a couple of days, and released her.

Veronica tried apologizing to her daughter, but she decided to spend the majority of time with her father and his new fiancée. Her son would occasionally stay with her but would spend most of his time in his room playing video games.

Her therapist saw her when she was in crisis, but Veronica avoided regular visits. The therapist encouraged her to follow up with the physician and stay on the medications. Her physician also urged her to stay on the medication combination that'd worked so well, stressing the need for her to get counseling. It'd work for a while until she decided to stop both. Her pattern was fixed.

Veronica was taken aback when her therapist and physician, who had spoken with each other about her, shared with her that they felt that she had not only bipolar disorder but also had borderline personality disorder. When she looked it up, she was shocked and saddened they would think that about her, since she just didn't see it and felt judged. Her therapist told her that there were effective specialized types of psychotherapy such as dialectical behavioral therapy (DBT), and the physician explained that medications were an important part of the solution but not the whole solution, since both often are better than either alone.

The physician explained she had all the factors that lead to mood disorders. When he took a detailed family history initially there was obvious addiction and mental illness on both sides of the family. He pointed out she had worsened at certain times of life, such as puberty, premenstrual, postpartum, and now pre-menopause in her early 40s. He explained it needed to be taken seriously since it could potentially get worse when she reached menopause. That could be fully supported if she stayed compliant with her treatment plan.

The third reason, situational stressors, became apparent due to Veronica's turbulent upbringing, her divorce following an unstable relationship with her ex-husband, her struggles with her children, parents, and friends, and her continued erratic relationships with both men and, for the most part, women.

Her therapist also noted that Veronica experienced cyclical mood changes, with the holiday season being the most challenging period, along with fluctuations during other times of the year. The therapist even suggested that Veronica might be dealing with love and relationship addiction, potentially coupled with sexual addiction. However, Veronica resented being labeled this way, just as she had with her borderline diagnosis, feeling unfairly judged.

Over the past few years, Veronica went through a series of relationships, with some partners making her believe that they were "the one," to the extent that some proposed living together, including their children if necessary. However, this arrangement bothered her own children, as they preferred not to be at her place when her boyfriend's children were present.

Veronica's children also didn't want to be around her when she was frequently drinking, as they knew she became uncontrollable and difficult to be around at those times. By this point, they were simply fed up with it.

Veronica felt a deep anger about her failed marriage, her children's reluctance to be with her, and her inability to find a stable, supportive partner. She actively avoided counseling sessions and often started and stopped medications, even though they had proven effective in the past. A part of her knew that she felt better when she took them, but she was convinced that the solution was a steady, enduring relationship.

When her ex-husband, Jack, got married, things took a turn for the worse. Veronica had always held out hope that they might become a family again. She missed the earlier years when her children were growing up, and life seemed relatively stable. She did not like the woman he was marrying and was upset by her daughter's implication that she had bonded with this new woman, and that her son also seemed to like the new arrangement.

On the night of Jack's wedding, Veronica spent it alone at home, drinking and crying over the situation. She had recently broken up with a man whom she believed was again "the one," but he, like others before him, left when things got tough. It was also the start of the holiday season, which was the time of year she dreaded the most since her depression typically worsened towards the year's end.

She consulted her psychologist, who urged her to visit her physician to resume her medications. Despite Veronica's belief that nothing could help her in these circumstances, the doctor assured her that addressing the medical aspect would make her feel better and stronger, enabling her to cope better with stressors. The doctor reminded her that every time she restarted her medications, she felt better and emphasized that the medications did not control her; instead, they helped her regain control.

The doctor encouraged her to quit drinking and explained how the medications could aid her by improving her mood and reducing her cravings for alcohol and tranquilizers. Still, Veronica couldn't see how anything, including medications and counseling, could assist her in her current situation. As she had done during their earlier visit, the doctor asked if she had any suicidal thoughts or plans, and she once again told him, "No."

Veronica tried to make plans with her children for Halloween and Thanksgiving but learned they already had commitments, resulting in minimal time together. She pleaded with them to visit on Christmas Eve, but they could only stay briefly on Christmas Day, as they had other obligations.

She faced New Year's Eve and the coming year alone, harboring an idea she had been contemplating for a while. She hadn't disclosed her plans to anyone, and nobody knew about her online research into effective suicide methods. She had learned from her past experience that overdosing was not a sure thing.

Unwilling to see her therapist or physician because her mind was made up, Veronica was determined not to be talked out of it. She believed there was no other way out of her situation. Although she knew her children would be upset, she believed it would be better for them if she were no longer in their lives.

Veronica yearned to be a wife and mother, but she felt that she had failed in both roles and that the other woman would be better off. Her relationship with her parents had been strained over the years and never truly improved, so she knew they wouldn't miss her. She tried to think of anyone in her life who would genuinely care but could think of nobody.

Veronica spent New Year's Eve by herself since nobody else contacted her about any plans. She had plans of her own, though.

She drank the best liqueurs she had. Veronica cried uncontrollably and wanted her pain to stop. She had researched different methods and decided on one certain to work. She was afraid it would hurt, so she drank enough to mask any pain.

She learned online how to find the type of rope and how to apply the ligature around her neck. She'd do it over the railing. It'd be high enough. She didn't want to be found days later, so she called Jack and left him a message. "Come to my house as soon as you get this. Tell whoever cared I'm sorry but you're all better off without me."

After she tied the rope over the second story railing, she jumped over the top of the staircase. For several seconds, she choked and grabbed for her neck until she lost consciousness. By the time Jack arrived her body was hanging limply. He sobbed and screamed until the paramedics arrived, but it was far too late. She was finally at peace.

PART FIVE

Why I Love My Job

"Hello, I am Dr. Paul Corona."

Obviously, this book is not an autobiography. Nevertheless, in this chapter and the next I am going to share pieces of my life's story with you. I am convinced that if you know the man behind the Corona Protocol, you will not only have a better understanding of what it is and how it works, but you'll also appreciate my passion for getting the word out to everyone who needs to hear there's relief for the misery they've unnecessarily endured.

I'll admit it's embarrassing to make public some of what I reveal in the following chapter. However, if you feel you're alone in your battle with anxiety, depression, bipolar disorder, or obsessive-compulsive disorder, it may be a great relief to discover that others have been through the same ordeal and perhaps worse episodes than your own–a doctor who has spent the majority of his professional life researching and treating mood disorders.

Part one of my story in this chapter covers how my early life was the precursor to my medical training, which in turn became the seedbed of my venture into the source and treatment of mood disorders.

We doctors refer to modern science as rational trial and error. We observe a phenomenon, extrapolate information from it, and come up with a hypothesis or theory. We test our theory by running relevant experiments that will either prove or disprove it. In some cases, it's only after many experiments and copious research that we can confirm our theory to be fact rather than hypothesis.

The Corona Protocol was formulated in the same way and has proven to be both a revolutionary diagnostic test and medical solution.

We're going to look into specific aspects of the brain and nervous system's neurochemistry.[1] This overview reveals several astonishing discoveries regarding positive changes that can be produced in our neurochemistry through the application of psychotropic medications.

This is not conjecture or theory, but science that can be seen in living tissue through electron microscopes.

---

[1]Neurochemicals (chemical molecules) are one of the ways brain cells (neurons) and nerve cells throughout our bodies communicate with each other. They're involved in every thought, emotion, movement, and experience coming through our five senses. Neurons also communicate with each other through electrical charges and are dependent on the interactions of neurochemicals.

Back To the Good Ol' Days

As a child, I had an insatiable curiosity about my world. I was fortunate to have parents who allowed me the freedom to explore and figure out how things worked, whether natural or mechanical. By grade school, I was fascinated by anything that required developing a strategy, such as games, puzzles, and chess. Before I entered 5th grade, I was playing in chess tournaments and ranked nationally. When my 5th grade social studies teacher challenged me to a chess match, my victory made it to the school newspaper, and even the local news. It was natural that my interest in strategy, especially as it related to chess, led to a love of math, and later, to science. To this day, my all-time favorite teacher was Mr. Dale, who taught 6th grade math. I remember I wanted to be a mathematician and inventor like my hero, Leonardo Da Vinci.

My curiosity never diminished. After high school, I set out on a course of education in biology and pre-med at the University of Southern California. I did not restrict myself to the "hard sciences" of the medical field, venturing into the "soft science" of human psychology. This was before the advanced technology of PET Scans, fMRIs, and other advanced imaging. Like several of my peers, I was fascinated by the human mind and the wide range of behavior.

Disorders of the mind concerned me as much as disorders of the body. I wanted explanations for why people behave as they do. I saw how genetics, early attachments, upbringing, trauma, and the effects of injury or illness affected the development of personality traits and mental instability. I've been fortunate that my drive to learn has never diminished. I'm convinced it sharpened my focus on my studies through medical school.

Later, at New York Medical College, the pace of our science studies accelerated, as did our workload in class and the labs. While working on my medical major, I took up classes in psychology and worked rotations in psychiatric care. Ultimately, it was the numerous and varied aspects of medicine that pulled me into Family Practice rather than Psychiatry.

Family practice is the front line of health care. When patients must be referred to specialists, the family physician must know something about orthopedics, cardiology, neurology, and pulmonary medicine in order to know when to refer and to whom. For me, treating my patient's bodies won out over treating their mental health issues. I discovered my passion was to help heal and improve the physical conditions of adults and children, the real people who could receive help from my studies.

I enjoyed living in New York, but it was great returning to California for my three-year residency program at California Medical Center in downtown Los Angeles. During this time, I met my beautiful and talented wife, Denise. Toward the end of my training, we married and moved to South Orange County, where I began my career in private practice.

I carried something with me my attending physician said during my residency. "Paul," he said, "half of the patients you will see in your private practice will come to you because of stress." His statement came back repeatedly, motivating me to observe how stress might be a factor in patients' complaints.

230

Soon it became clear the degree stress affects our lives in general. It dawned on me my attending physician's estimation was far too conservative. Stress, as either the cause of the complaint or a significant factor accounting for the number of patients entering my office, was more like eighty percent. This became the epiphany that turned my attention toward researching the ways emotional states influence the effectiveness of the body's organs and various systems.

Early Encounters with Severe Challenges

Many large, metropolitan hospitals have a "locked ward"—a psychiatric wing dedicated to patients with severe mental distress and in some instances may include drug addiction or alcoholism. Those are people who have lost their capacity to function in the world outside. When I walked into one of those units for the first time, it felt like I had been transported to a different planet. The people were kept under lock and key. Visitation was restricted to doctors and hospital staff with only a few exceptions.

To be placed in a locked ward, patients had to be deemed a danger to themselves or others. Patients generally wind up there after exhibiting irrational behavior, talking nonsense, or because they have stopped communicating altogether. Some of them (in California) enter the hospital under a Welfare code referred to as a "fifty-one-fifty," in which police officers are permitted to place them there against their will until they are evaluated, and a determination is made regarding the severity of their symptoms.

My role in the locked unit was to conduct an initial examination, interview, and evaluation of incoming patients. I would discuss my findings with the resident psychiatrist or whoever was on-call. We'd determine a diagnosis and course of treatment.

The interview took place in a small, sterile room where I sat alone with the patient. As we walked through the hallways to the designated area, we heard screaming and gibberish talking. One time, an interviewee told me he was Jesus Christ. "It's an honor to meet you," I responded.

Trying to reason with patients whose minds are spinning outside of reality is futile. Humor can sometimes get through or ease the tension. They were usually more cooperative when I acted as though I were taking them seriously. After introducing himself, the patient said to me, "By the way, there's a man standing on your head." I felt embarrassed after reflexively looking up at the ceiling.

You learn about cases like this from textbooks and lectures, but spending time in those first interviews was disturbing. I wondered how the mind could become so broken and alien. I thought: "What happened to this person to make him so sick? How much stress did it take for her to finally snap? What trauma, illness, or injury did this person suffer to become so delusional and detached from reality?"

After getting over the heartache of seeing human persons, some of whom looked normal as though they belonged out in the world, I became intrigued. I experienced strange illnesses I'd never seen up close. I was deeply moved at my patients' plight and wanted to explore the neurological mechanisms maintaining sanity and how they break down to discover, if possible, whether there were ways to support such tragedies. I continued researching the neurology of psychosis during my first year of private practice.

I opened myself to researching neuroscience—a field that didn't exist until modern imaging technology allowed us to examine the functions of a living brain. The explosion of information that's become available in the last thirty years has shed a light regarding the onset of many mental illnesses like schizophrenia, Alzheimer's, Autism Spectrum Disorder, and Parkinson's disease.

We have a better understanding of anxiety, depression, bipolar disorder, and obsessive-compulsive disorder. Visiting patients who have suffered the worst symptoms of mental disorders has given me greater empathy for all my patients, but also fired up my determination to find and improve the best treatments for them.

What My Patients Have Taught Me About Stress

Henry came to the office for his annual physical examination, a requirement for his job. The first concern that caught my attention was his elevated blood pressure, notably high for a man in his early thirties. A review of his medical history revealed that this was the first time his blood pressure had spiked to such levels, and there were no other risk factors in his health or family history. Henry's restlessness and irritability were evident in his body language and demeanor.

I asked him about his life. "Please be completely honest," I said.

"Well, work is really challenging and there's a lot of tension with my boss," Henry said. "And there's a lot of miscommunications between me and my wife."

The conventional approach to treating high blood pressure focuses on symptom management, a critical step due to the potential life-threatening complications associated with hypertension. However, symptom management doesn't address the root causes of the issue.

Instead of prescribing medication and sending Henry on his way, I inquired, "Do you have a trusted friend or mentor with whom you can discuss your troubles?"

"Maybe my pastor," he said.

"You should reach out," I said. We talked about the importance of exercise and how controlled physical activity could help reduce anxiety. I explained the effectiveness of deep breathing techniques, such as using the diaphragm to take slow, deep breaths when anxiety became acute, particularly during difficult conversations with his wife and boss. Henry attentively considered my suggestions, and we scheduled a follow-up appointment for a month later.

But why did I focus on teaching Henry breathing techniques? In the 1960s and 70s, medical researchers became intrigued by the impact of different breathing patterns on physical and mental functions. Breathing techniques gained attention, partly due to the shift towards natural childbirth. Expecting mothers of the previous generation were heavily medicated and often unconscious during childbirth, only meeting their babies hours later. This prompted new approaches like those recommended by Robert Bradley in his 1965 book, "Husband Coached Childbirth," which empowered mothers through breathing patterns, granting them more control over the birthing process.

Breathing techniques can have a profound impact on pain and discomfort management. By focusing on the breath, we alter brain activity, disrupting loops of anxious or depressive thoughts. Shifting attention to breathing can help people control strong impulses to engage in unwanted habits, such as smoking, losing temper, or abandoning important projects.

A month later, Henry returned to the office with a cheerful smile. He shared constructive developments at work and with his wife, crediting the suggestions I'd given him. His conversation with the pastor had been helpful, and he felt meaningfully better. Most importantly, his blood pressure had returned to a healthy range without medication.

Reflecting on Henry's case, I considered how his blood pressure had correlated with periods of heightened stress. When his stress levels subsided, his blood pressure normalized. This prompted me to question the relationship between stress and various health issues, especially hypertension, and whether reducing stress could have a significant impact on patients' health without the need for increased medication dosages, or even the need for medication at all.

Upon closer examination of my patients, I discovered a clear pattern: stress had a domino effect on their well-being. Emotional distress placed a physical burden on the body, resulting in frequent visits to our office. Moreover, these visits often entailed more severe symptoms and complaints.

Stress is an inescapable part of life, affecting us in various contexts like family, work, and daily activities. Researchers have coined the term "eustress" to describe moderate stress associated with good health. However, stress becomes harmful when it escalates and becomes unmanageable. Stressors can include family and workplace issues, travel, tests, exercise, and the everyday challenges we face.

It's crucial for healthcare providers to consider the impact of stress and explore ways to alleviate it, as it's closely linked to various health conditions. By recognizing and addressing stress, we may improve patients' overall well-being and reduce the need for excessive medication.

Stress becomes harmful if any of the following conditions apply:

* The amount of a single stressor becomes too great to manage.

* The presence of too many stressors at one time.

* We have not learned how to manage moderate stress and therefore overreact to our daily stressors.

* Another condition, such as anxiety or depression, is also present.

* Poor or inadequate coping skills.

* An underlying personality disorder.

Stress takes a toll on our bodies, demanding more from our resources. It doesn't just affect our mood but can also weaken our immune system, making us more susceptible to illnesses, injuries, migraines, and allergens. For those living with chronic illnesses like diabetes, Crohn's Disease, or fibromyalgia, the burden of stress can often exceed their tolerance threshold. In such situations, the ability to respond to stress effectively can alleviate some of that pressure.

Fortunately, there are medications available to alleviate the physical discomfort associated with low stress tolerance, manage chronic illness symptoms, and reduce stress responses. If you've been prescribed medication for any of these conditions, it's best to continue with the treatment, even if you feel it could be more effective.

However, I eventually questioned whether traditional treatments were the only or best way to meet the needs of my patients, particularly when medications come with severe side effects. Early on, I had an inkling that there must be another approach, one that could provide more than symptom relief and enhance their quality of life. Henry's case gave me the chance to test my "educated intuition," exploring unconventional but scientifically sound treatments.

It's hard to believe three decades have passed since Henry walked into my office, distressed and unhappy. Many patients visited us with health concerns, primarily focusing on physical discomfort, aches, and pains. They rarely mentioned feelings of depression or anxiety, although signs of emotional distress were often clear in physical symptoms like fatigue, low energy, motivation issues, digestive problems, and sleep disorders. When patients only report these physical symptoms, and doctors address only the physical aspects, emotional issues contributing to their complaints often go untreated.

Henry's case taught me the importance of understanding patients' emotional states to maximize the effectiveness of addressing their physical concerns. This shift prompted me to ask more comprehensive questions about their mood and stress tolerance, expanding our conversations to consider their well-being as a whole.

Betty

When Betty came to our office, her emotional distress triggered empathy in me. I handed her a box of tissues, and through her tears and sobs, she shared her overwhelming grief over the loss of her sister, which left her incapacitated. While distinguishing deep grief from clinical depression is challenging, Betty's suffering was genuine, and her symptoms were real. It's common for people to experience a year or two of painful grief after losing a loved one, but Betty's grief hadn't lessened in a year, which concerned me.

Betty had no history of depression or anxiety, so we began with the usual recommendations: diet, exercise, counseling, and grief support groups. However, I also suggested trying a low dose of Zoloft, an antidepressant that had been found effective. Betty was initially hesitant, fearing the medication might suppress her grief. I explained the medication aimed to address her depression, not her grief, which was related to her sister's loss but had evolved into a chronic condition with additional symptoms interfering with her daily life. Betty agreed to try it.

Two weeks later, Betty returned for her follow-up appointment, visibly more at ease. Her improved posture and self-confidence were evident. The medication not only lifted her depression but also alleviated her worries, repetitive thoughts, sleep disturbances, and panic attacks. The marked improvement prompted me to explore further how one mood disorder can manifest other emotional and physical symptoms, shedding light on the intricate connection between the mind and the body

238

Discovering The Power of Healing the Body by Treating the Mind

While working with patients indicating that stress influenced their physical or emotional health, I discovered the importance of identifying the most significant stressor(s). Several reasons underlie the significance of this in deciding the treatment course for each patient. For instance, it helps to determine whether the patient's primary stressor is short-term or long-term. A short-term concern could involve delivering a company presentation or a forthcoming necessary flight, while a long-term worry might revolve around a years-long outstanding debt.

Another consideration relates to the nature of the stressor, whether it's personal and close to home. For example, dealing with a divorce or caring for a loved one suffering from a chronic, debilitating, or terminal illness is a personal stressor, while impersonal stressors could involve, for instance, an expensive car repair.

The mood disorder itself is another type of stressor. Anxiety or depression often leads individuals to question themselves, wondering why they can't be like friends who don't grapple with these emotional issues. Identifying the source of stress provided valuable information to develop a treatment plan. It enabled me to assess whether the patient's stress resulted from a temporary situation or had become a habitual response to daily life. Stress triggered by a test or performance obligation disappears when the task concludes, but chronic stress from an anxiety or depressive disorder persists. Patients struggle to break free from a cycle of repetitive thoughts.

The difference lies between situational stressors like holiday preparations, job loss, or family conflicts, and coping with persistent depression, panic attacks, insomnia, or an eating disorder. These distinctions transformed my conversations with patients, motivating me to explore more than just physical symptoms.

As the link between emotional well-being and physical health became clear, I began seeking the various moods stemming from stress affecting patients, amplifying, or exacerbating their ailments. This led me to develop a more comprehensive family history questionnaire, request more specific details during interviews, and improve my listening skills. I became alert to times when patients omitted information or were less than truthful, not due to intentional deceit but because they may have considered some symptoms unimportant or felt embarrassed about sharing them.

It is not that patients intentionally lie to their doctors, but there are symptoms they feel are unimportant or that they are embarrassed to share with someone else. This is especially true if in any way their doctor has displayed a judgmental attitude toward patients or others (sadly, this is all too common, and some doctors do this unconsciously). People do not want to be scolded for conditions that they may know or imagine they have brought on themselves.

Betty's case was a turning point in my approach to patient healthcare. It became evident that the complex relationship between mood disorders and the body's impact required a deep understanding of brain science. Human experience remains intricately connected to the ceaseless activity within the brain. Every thought, emotion, breath, and heartbeat engage neurons. The brain is an astonishingly complex and delicate entity, easily disrupted by even the slightest issues, leading to sight, speech, hearing, movement, and social impairments.

Systems within the brain overlap, making it an integrated entity. Emotions trigger physiological responses, such as an increase in heart rate and respiration controlled by the vagus nerve, showing how a chemical reaction in the brain

240

can disrupt the nervous system. In this fully integrated organism, emotions affect the body, and the body, in turn, influences emotions.

With mood disorders, the brain draws on the body's resources to maintain its stability, including immune system functions, but these systems can eventually deplete. The toll emotions take on us becomes apparent in symptoms that reach the level of consciousness. Short-term, intense emotions may result in erratic breathing, sore throats, nausea, shakiness, clumsiness, and forgetfulness. For long-term negative emotions, symptoms may include headaches, joint pain, stomachaches, low energy, and a reduced tolerance for noise or others' voices.

In medical school, our focus was on diagnosing health issues, predominantly based on physical symptoms. Even when studying pathology and the etiology of patients' conditions, the primary emphasis remained on physical causes. However, I found that improving a patient's mood yielded positive outcomes in addressing their chronic pain and other bodily complaints.

Of course, I knew something about brain chemistry, because clinical neuroanatomy was one of my required disciplines in med school. However, when doctors are preoccupied with bones, organs, muscles, and skin, we don't always look closely at cellular activity. We know whatever occurs in the body takes place at a cellular level–after all, the body is always at war with germs and bacteria–but it's not necessary to focus on what's taking place in the body's cells when putting a cast over a broken bone.

I discovered that during the time it takes for a broken bone to heal, the quality of healing can be affected by what's taking place in the patient's brain cells. That's just one small piece of the cellular puzzle.

Each human experience is connected to the nonstop activity that is going on inside the brain. Sight, sound, smell, taste, and touch involve chemical actions and electrical charges in individual brain cells, linking them to thousands of other brain cells.[2] Tens of thousands of brain cells are activated when we perform a movement as simply picking up a glass of water and moving it toward our mouths. Neurons are activated with every thought, emotion, breath, and heartbeat. The brain is the most amazing, complex, fragile, delicately balanced, and intricate device in the known universe. Even the tiniest rupture, aneurysm, vitamin or mineral deficiency, injury, or obstruction can cause serious impairment to sight, speech, hearing, movement, sociability, and more.

In medical school we learned to diagnose health problems, focusing primarily on the physical symptoms. Even when our education turned to pathology, the etiology of a patient's condition—that is, what caused the condition remained a mystery. Our study still focused on physical causes. I discovered improving a patient's mood resulted in positive outcomes in terms of chronic pain and other complaints regarding their bodily symptoms.

---

[2]See *Healing the Mind and Body*, 2007, pgs. 63-67 for a full yet simple explanation of the science of how neurochemicals move from one brain cell to another, creating a chain reaction through a cluster of neurons, and how the process affects thoughts, emotions, and moods.

242

Discovering Significant Improvement
with Slight Adjustments

Unlike Henry, Betty's symptoms couldn't be eased by learning relaxation and breathing techniques—at least, not at first. Many people have suffered too long and are simply too wound up to be able to benefit directly from therapy or relaxation exercises. Betty's first step was figuring out a way to unblock whatever was keeping her in a loop of negative thoughts and feelings, preventing her from getting better and moving forward.

Of the multitude of neurochemicals used by the brain and nervous system, most mood disorders can be successfully treated by addressing four of them, or, as I refer to them: the Fantastic Four neurochemicals. The first to come to my attention was Serotonin.

Serotonin is utilized by the body to aid the digestive system, including digestion and nausea. Serotonin plays a role in falling asleep and waking up.

Healthy bones and sexual function depend on Serotonin. Serotonin is a key factor regulating positive and stable moods. Researchers have discovered the body uses the amino acid tryptophan to produce Serotonin. People whose diets are low in tryptophan may suffer from a Serotonin deficiency, which is one of the chemical conditions that can result in depression or anxiety.

A much more common problem occurs when there's an ample supply of Serotonin in the brain, but for some reason, it doesn't move successfully from one neuron to the next.[3] Another chemical imbalance related to Serotonin

---

[3]For more detailed information on this neurochemical failure, and how Selective Serotonin Reuptake Inhibitors (SSRIs) address these problems, see Corona, Ibid, pgs. 83-96

happens when Serotonin and Dopamine levels skyrocket. The patient will experience mania and a potential break with reality (psychosis).

When I first began treating patients with medications designed to resolve Serotonin issues, I was astounded at how well they worked. Betty was an early example of someone who responded quickly and positively to an SSRI medication. At that time, the leading medications were, in order of their appearance on the market, Prozac, Zoloft, and Paxil.

Discovering the value and limitations of these medications became an important part of the Corona Protocol Puzzle, demonstrating how resolving a set of psychological symptoms could also solve specific physical symptoms.

I felt we were making good progress with the arrival of antidepressants and anti-anxiety medications, but the effectiveness of my patient care took a quantum leap when Effexor XR[4] hit the market. Initially, to achieve an adequate dosage, Effexor had to be taken twice a day. Patients endured temporary nausea after each dose. With gradual time-release capsules, patients only had to take one dose a day and didn't experience regular nausea.

Effexor also helped another neurotransmitter critical for a healthy brain and positive moods: Norepinephrine.

Effexor XR vastly improved my patients' lives. Over the following thirty years, I have observed their stress levels decrease. Their moods were greatly enhanced, and many somatic symptoms got resolved, including neck, shoulder, and upper back pain; headaches and the debilitating pain of TMJ; joint and muscle pain; and digestive and abdominal discomfort from irritable bowel syndrome and related irregularities.

---

[4]XR stands for "extended release," which means the medication is gradually introduced into the patient's system.

Conservatively, the impact of this medication on the effectiveness of my approach to medicine was significant. Not so conservatively. I'll say the impact was monumental.

Once The Bell Is Rung, You Can't Un-Ring It

From that point on, there was no going back. The positive improvement in physical symptoms while treating stress and mood disorders meant I couldn't neglect patient's mental health. Ignoring the interaction between the mind and body in treating individuals could be a detriment to their health and well-being. I reevaluated every patient we were treating. This entailed a more thorough observation than in my previous years. The new commitment was an original approach and one that remains unknown or undervalued.

Psychiatrists, unlike psychologists, must have a medical degree as well as degrees in psychology and psychotherapy. The medical degree is crucial for understanding the neurological disruptions caused by a variety of factors, including normal hormonal changes, head injury or brain disease, tumor, stroke, aneurysm, alcoholism, or drug addiction, and more.

Most Psychiatrists provide little or no talk therapy, but merely prescribe medications. Most lean heavily on their education in psychology and often neglect the patient's current physical condition. Although patients may fill out a form regarding any health issues or medications they're taking for physical issues, most psychiatrists accept what their clients tell them rather than probe into their physical health with any depth.

Also, patients may be reluctant to tell the psychiatrist all they're experiencing in their bodies because they don't see the relevance of revealing those things to someone who's there to work with their mind.

Patients need to be educated about the dynamics between mind and body interactions, otherwise important clues to their mental health may go undetected and unresolved. Primary care doctors don't receive the same intensive education in psychology as the psychiatrist, but many do begin with an undergraduate degree in psychology, or like me, a degree in Biology with some psychology courses as electives.

Primary care providers tend to look mostly at physical factors—symptoms and causation—and do not pay as much attention to the patient's mental health. If a mood disorder comes to the attention of the family physician, or if the symptoms are consistent with a stress-related diagnosis, one of two approaches will be taken.

One approach is referring the patient to a psychologist or psychiatrist. In the best possible situation, the physician and therapist will collaborate on the patient's symptoms and care. Another approach a primary physician is prescribing a psychotropic medication to treat the suspected mood disorder.

Pharmaceutical companies have flooded the market with a plethora of medications. What criteria will the medical doctor use for choosing the right one? For some doctors, it'll be the most recent medication on the market. For others, it'll be the one they always use at the beginning. For others, it will be the medication samples available from a sales rep. The majority of family doctors don't feel they have the time to study all of the medications and their various indications to treat mood disorders.[5] Like many doctors, I assumed the medications that supported the re-uptake of Serotonin were the best answer in treating most depressive and anxiety disorders.

---

[5] For this reason, I have provided a streamlined guide for physicians that provide a synopsis of the underlying factors of all the available medications in Volume 3 of *Healing the Mind and Body.*

Until I witnessed how the positive outcome of Effexor XR catapulted over other Serotonin medications, I didn't know there was something better.

Not only did their mood improve, but physical symptoms were either reduced or completely resolved. Statistically, one out of three patients improved when Serotonin alone was treated. After adding Norepinephrine, two out of three patients showed marked improvement. For me, this breakthrough was so significant I assumed it would be written up in every medical journal and presented in countless psychiatric conferences.

Unfortunately, as far as primary doctors and psychiatrists go, the medications that address Serotonin alone are still the first-line agents used to treat depression and anxiety disorders. To my knowledge, I was the first doctor to use a medication that addresses Serotonin and Norepinephrine as first-line agents and Serotonin only medications as second-line agents. Even formal psychiatric recommendations from textbooks, journals, and other relevant sources disregard the importance of balancing norepinephrine and serotonin simultaneously. This is heartbreaking, since countless patients over the decades have not been treated in the best possible way, resulting in significant unnecessary suffering.

With three decades of experience treating patients with mood disorders on Effexor XR, or more recently Pristiq ER, my hope is to change the outdated thinking of my colleagues regarding their first approach treatment.

What I am about to say is so important, it deserves its own paragraph.

The medications have a cumulative effect. A residual of each dose stays in the body's system, so if the dosage isn't increased, there's still an increased amount daily until the body can regulate it.

Here's a brief outline of the problem doctors and psychiatrists face. Mood altering medications (I prefer "mood-normalizing") are believed to be most effective when taken at the highest recommended dose.

When Effexor XR first came out, the manufacturer released the two-week "starter packs" that were offered to our patients, which suggested doctors begin at the lowest dose for the first week, then increase to the second lowest dose for the second week. The company recommended the dose be increased to the highest dosage range within the following month.

This proved to be inappropriate for most patients. At the higher dosage range, the side effects outweighed the benefits. This caused considerable damage since many doctors felt it was an effective medication with too many side effects, leading to Its nickname: "Side-Effexor." Most doctors went back to their SSRI first-line mentality. I believe the damage this caused has been incalculable.

This is the trade-off we look for when adjusting medications. As long as the benefits are great enough to make the side effects tolerable or irrelevant, we're comfortable with continuation.

We found our patients experienced optimum benefit from the medication by the end of the second week of the two-row starter pack before considering a written prescription. Another happy surprise was some patients reported substantial progress and, in some cases, optimal results within the first week. The majority of patients haven't required an increase in dosage after the second week, finding the dosage perfect.

It's critical the prescribing physician monitors the patient diligently in the first two or three weeks, listening carefully to their comments. The beauty of the process is that we can always explore other options. But the answers are usually found in the details. If there are any early significant adverse responses to the medication, we back the patient off. If after a week or two the patient is feeling just "A little bit better," we increase the dosage to see if we can get further improvement.

Some do well at the highest doses without any significant side effects. Whenever patients report good results, we hold them at that dose. This process of individualizing treatment plans is one facet of the Corona Protocol—an important one, to be sure, but the complete program is necessary to realize the results we hope to see.

Other Clinical Insights That Came Later

Stress is a major cause of physical problems and complaints. The second lesson was that mood-normalizing medications couldn't only relieve stress, but also resolve many somatic symptoms, such as achiness, intestinal discomfort, muscle and joint soreness, headaches, and more.

The third lesson was finding out the combined effectiveness of balancing Serotonin and Norepinephrine in Effexor XR was many times more effective in addressing the emotional issues and physical complaints associated with mood disorders.

The fourth insight gained while prescribing Effexor XR was that the manufacturers' recommended doses were too aggressive. The majority of patients couldn't tolerate increasing the medication too high, too fast.[6]

Working with pharmaceutical companies' representatives and upper levels of management became a source of great frustration. They were allowed to disclose only the specific results of their own clinical trials. This meant they couldn't tell primary care physicians about the somatic symptom reduction and anti-anxiety benefits of using their mood-

---

[6]I'll summarize the average optimal dosing. The second lowest dose of 75 mg is the average dose, with the lowest dose of 37.5 mg the second most common. 150 mg comes in third place, with 225 mg fourth and 300 mg in last place. This completely goes against the original company guidelines.

normalizing medications, nor could they go beyond their literature in recommending the fast-track strategy of rushing patients to the "full dosage."

Their resistance to looking into cutting edge applications of their medications, the impact it could have in the field of medicine, and the amount of good it could offer our patients, was confusing. It made no sense they'd not jump on real-life insights. Attending lectures, seminars, and conferences, I couldn't find another doctor who'd seen the kind of rapid results my patients were enjoying. I surmised that the reason was they weren't looking for it.

Pharmaceutical companies hire medical professionals to give lectures and answer questions regarding their products in conferences prepared for prescribing physicians. For a while, I was the only family practitioner among a sea of psychiatrists trained to give lectures. Unfortunately, I was instructed to stick to the script, because Federal law prohibits companies from suggesting their medications could be used effectively for treating other disorders besides those printed on the label, modifying the message about the dosing, and suggesting other creative "off label" ways of working with psychotropic medicines.

Even still, I said as much as I could while respecting the guidelines of each company, for the most part. But it was frustrating. I was desperate to share with healthcare communities' insights I'd learned and the incredible improvement I'd seen with my patients. It was painful holding back because the insights could've changed the trajectory of millions of suffering patients.

Two Remarkable Outcomes

Why am I intensely passionate about the Corona Protocol? Because I've seen the difference it can make in a person's life like it did for Peter. After two back surgeries, Peter had little relief from shooting pain that went down his legs due to an impingement of his sciatic nerve. If you've never experienced sciatica pain or know someone who has, it's difficult comprehending the severity. If these patients are fortunate, they might be able to find a position to find relief. Otherwise, they're always miserable when walking, standing, sitting, and lying down.

After each surgery, Peter could go through two or three months before he was in agony again. He told me he was preparing for another surgery, along with recovery and rehabilitation. He needed a respite. Desperate for another opinion, he came to our office.

After sharing his story with me, I said, "I have an idea for a treatment plan. It's new and innovative, but I am fairly certain it could work. At the least it will not make your condition worse."

"Wow. I want to know more," Pete said.

I explained the role of the brain's chemistry and how it can affect the entire nervous system.

We explored his stress level.

"I have a family to feed and clothe, but my battle with pain is so stressful," he admitted.

"I assured you it's not your fault you're under so much stress. It's all unmanageable," I said. "You're suffering in an agonizing loop of physical pain, which is causing emotional distress, and isn't helping your physical pain. You cannot separate the mind and body. They are intimately connected."

I introduced him to an antidepressant—Effexor XR, my silver bullet medication.

He was skeptical. "But I'm not depressed!"

However, he agreed his sciatic condition had definitely impacted the quality of his life.

I was convinced this would prove to be the ideal medication for Peter, so he agreed to try it and return in two weeks for a follow-up. I instructed him to call me after the first week so we could reevaluate the dosage. After a week on the smallest dosage, he reported, "My pain's gone down a little."

"Great," I said. "Let's increase the dosage a step higher."

When we met the next week, Peter's attitude took me by surprise. He was visibly upset, and he let me know right away that I was the cause. I couldn't understand what could have triggered him, especially because he confirmed his pain had been relieved ninety percent. In fact, I did not take him seriously at first because I assumed he was joking.

He showed me his MRI photographs and pointed to the scar tissue and blockages on his spinal column, the source of his excruciating pain. "Don't you get it? I have real pain! I'm not crazy."

"You certainly do. And you're holding the proof. But I already knew your pain had a physical cause," I said. "Effexor XR can soothe nerve pain by supporting chemical activity within the nerve cells and avoid blockages. There's no better way to address your pain than by getting inside the largest nerve in our bodies, the sciatic nerve, and balancing its neurochemicals."

He understood and I continued. "Assisting your sciatic nerve will enable it to function effectively all the way to the bottom of both of your legs. My goal is one hundred percent recovery or relief. To get to that mark, I recommended you take over-the-counter ibuprofen as an anti-inflammatory, and acetaminophen."

A brief time later, I was thrilled to learn Peter cancelled his back surgery.

His surgeon was relieved he wouldn't have to perform a procedure that produced poor results. To this day, Peter's quality of life is greatly enhanced. He isn't having chronic pain, is back at work, and exercising again.

Peter's case was dramatic and unheard of regarding having chronic severe pain and with no history of depression. Reaching 90% recovery in two weeks using the antidepressant Effexor XR could rock a medical community perplexed by chronic and treatment resistant pain. Conditions for which there is no successful treatment, such as fibromyalgia, irritable bowel syndrome, chronic fatigue syndrome, autoimmune diseases, headaches, arthritis flareups, hypertension and more, could potentially be resolved or significantly reduced for the many patients using one small pill.

I wondered about the many ailments I tracked down using medical books and journals. I'd look for the most up-to-date research regarding some difficult to treat disorders or illnesses and kept running into the same words, "etiology unknown" at the end of each article. Not knowing a disease's cause means we don't know how to prevent or treat it.

It's frustrating. I'd read through a long, informative, well-researched paper, and then hit "etiology unknown." I'd ask, "After the money poured into countless lab hours and research, there's nothing I can do for these patients?"

I uncovered a link between a host of "etiology unknown" illnesses correlating with chemical imbalances in the nervous system. If neurochemical imbalances weren't the precise cause for all instances, it was certainly a contributing factor, pointing to hope for effective treatment. This made sense, and I wanted to broadcast it to the world of medicine.

We have come to a historic moment in the healthcare professions, where we can offer faith in combating these illnesses. It's a breakthrough worth celebrating. After all, these insights into the reciprocal interactions of physiology and psychology, body, and mind belong to the entire medical community, and by extension, to each patient. But old paradigms are difficult to overcome.

When I lectured to doctors, my audience was suspicious. Few professionals stood with me, nor could I find anyone discovering similar insights.

I explained to whoever would listen, "Stress causes and intensifies physical pain, physical pain causes and intensifies stress in a loop."

We'd passed the chicken or the egg conundrum. We didn't always need to answer the question of etiology. Figuring out which came first didn't matter. Suffering patients matter. We can go straight to the nerve cells and bring them relief. This is holistic medicine at its best helping the body heal itself. This is making effective use of the mind-body connection. It is both the chicken and the egg.

Flora

In the mid-1990s, Flora made her first visit to our office. Flora was sixty-two years old, with a long, painful history of severe rheumatoid disease. If you know anyone who has lived with this ailment, you know its misery.

Flora's twisted hands, the strain in her face, and her careful steps made her pain evident. My heart went out to her at once as I tried to fathom her discomfort.

"How are you mentally handling your condition?" I asked.

"Not good," Flora said. "I have the disease and a lot of stress. My husband's talking about us separating. It's all so much."

Stress is a significant factor for increased pain, along with emotionally coping with her circumstances. Her Rheumatologist had her on six Vicodin painkillers a day, more than the maximum recommended dose. Even still, the Vicodin was only taking the edge off, leaving her in great discomfort. Humira wouldn't reach the market for several years.

Having repeated successes with Effexor XR with chronic somatic symptoms, I started her on the recommended low dose, then bumped it up after the first week.

At her two-week follow-up appointment, Flora's remarkable improvement was pleasant news for us both.

"My pain's gone down a lot and I stopped the Vicodin. When I need a little more relief, I just take either ibuprofen, acetaminophen, or both," Flora said.

Flora's Rheumatologist turned out to be a really good and caring person. When he gave me his opinion on her progress, he asked, "Why is she so much better without her pain meds?"

"It has to do with neurochemicals in her brain not doing their job. The stress she carried interfered with them. It's great her pain's diminished and manageable, and her outlook on life has greatly improved," I said.

He appreciated hearing about how Effexor XR works on Serotonin and Norepinephrine, tied to her physical and emotional health. He told me that he wanted to learn how to use the same treatment for his other patients, especially those suffering similar to Flora. This was music to my ears. I was more than happy to share my findings.

Newer Medications and More Breakthrough Insights

For a long time, Effexor XR was my first-choice medication to address mood disorders, stress, and the physical symptoms that were caused or exacerbated by stress. Later, when Cymbalta became available, I prescribed it for patients who did not respond to Effexor XR as well as hoped, or who had complaints of specific chronic conditions such as fibromyalgia. In research trials, Cymbalta proved to be effective for these cases and in resolving other somatic symptoms. Some patients responded better to Cymbalta, but Effexor XR remained my medication of choice.

Most doctors didn't understand the power of an SNRI over an SSRI. I'd seen better efficacy with Effexor XR regarding anxiety reduction, somatic symptom reduction, and an overall better mood than SSRIs. I figured they'd see it was a *class effect* and that those who appreciated Cymbalta would also appreciate Effexor XR.

I'd been prescribing Effexor XR for 10 years by that point, so I wasn't surprised by the results seen with Cymbalta's debut. I don't have anything negative to say about Cymbalta—it is a good medication and several of our patients did well on it— but Effexor XR has proven to be more effective and with less side effects. I assumed other primary care physicians would see it as the better overall choice of the two medications. Unfortunately, I was wrong.

My frustration with the medical community reached a tipping point and drove me to act. I had to get the word out. So, in 2007 my first book *Healing the Mind and Body* was published. I documented everything I'd discovered during the years I'd been treating patients as whole people.

When a generic version of Effexor XR became available, I no longer received free samples to give patients. Many patients don't want to "experiment" with any medication they have to purchase when they cannot be guaranteed a quick and positive resolution to their problem. Some of that tension is removed if they're able to begin with free samples, enabling them to begin a trial period immediately. Another advantage in doing so keeps them from the pharmacy and the negative information they may provide the patient about the product.

Soon, a third medication in the same class as Effexor and Cymbalta was introduced, Pristiq ER. It's formulated by the same company that manufactured Effexor XR and is the most active metabolite of Effexor XR. They harnessed the best part of the product and created a new version. So, for the first half of my practice, Effexor XR was my first-line antidepressant, but in the second half, it's been Pristiq ER. In my opinion, these are the best medications ever invented for improving patient health by integrating the mind and body.

An Important Question

In my initial interview with patients, if they tell me they have been depressed or experienced intense anxiety, or if their symptoms indicate a mood disorder, or if I suspect an underlying mood disorder, there's a question I ask that immediately gives us both an important insight for developing a treatment plan. "As you recall, what was the happiest time in your life?"

It is surprising how many patients will answer it was when they were a child and in elementary school up until about eleven or twelve years old. For many people, the transition into adolescence, with the hormonal changes, the challenges of moving from childhood towards adulthood, including the process of individuation, and the rise of self-consciousness that's intensified by socialization within peer groups, the joys of childhood are lost or trampled to death.

An exception to childhood being the happiest time of life is if there was any type of abuse, the early loss of a parent or other loved one, divorce, or a severe childhood illness. The other most common answer is during the late teens into the early to mid-20s —a carefree time when life is simpler with less responsibilities. Some get stuck; life's not moving in the direction they'd hoped.

My next question is, "What if we could restore that season of happiness and make it a lifestyle?"

Some are incredulous while others ask, "Can we really do that?"

"That's the goal," I say. "I've seen it enough to know it's not only possible but probable."

If I am talking with patients who've already been on Effexor XR for six months to a year, and they've seen a definitive change in their health and emotional well-being but are far from feeling like they're living in the happiest season of their lives, I wonder if we've done all we could to achieve our goal.

I've never been content with "almost" or "good enough" when it comes to my patients. I don't override a patient's decision to plateau at a level that's, in my opinion, less than optimum. Instead, I'll try persuading them to take another step toward superior improvement. When a patient hit the upper limits of what Effexor XR could do and were doing "okay" but not "great," I had to find a way to push forward. In most cases, the solution was as simple as adding a new medication.

Susan, a middle-aged mom, experienced what I considered a more than 50% improvement in her fibromyalgia, headaches, and depressive symptoms with Effexor XR. She felt like she'd experienced 100% success.

She set the bar for her recovery much lower than my standards. We still needed to address her fatigue, lack of motivation and drive, improvement of her residual depressive symptoms and apathy, and a decrease in her already low sex drive. She also complained about her difficulty in focusing and with her short-term memory.

"I have a medication I know can help with those symptoms called Wellbutrin XL," I said.

After two weeks of Wellbutrin XL, Susan was ecstatic. "All my symptoms are gone. How can it be so simple after I've struggled for so long?"

"The combination of Effexor XR and Wellbutrin XL— which I refer to as the 'Dynamic Duo'—are the superheroes that saved the day!" I said.

The remarkable effects of the combination wasn't a surprise, but that it worked in one case after another was more than expected.

There was a good reason for the success of these medications in resolving mood disorders and physical symptoms. The early antidepressants targeted serotonin. The benefit of combining Effexor XR and Wellbutrin XL resulted in improvement because of the medication's effect on an additional neurochemical, specifically dopamine: the "Pleasure Chemical," and it balances norepinephrine to a lesser degree. I've found the extra boost of norepinephrine is a good fit with an SNRI, providing more complete results.

Addressing three out of the "Fantastic Four" primary chemicals involved in how our brains and bodies manage stress was an important breakthrough in a program of patient care already working wonders.

Adding Wellbutrin to Effexor sparked electrical and chemical activity within the brain that provided individuals an experience of energy that integrated the potentials of both mind and body when working together. This was the original "Corona Cocktail," and is still effective to this day.

Positive changes in my patients gives me the greatest satisfaction and pleasure of working in my profession, fueling my passion to continue pressing forward and increase my knowledge and enhance my skills. There've been times when my patient's enthusiastic reports moved me to tears.

For example, when Peter, who we met earlier, was two days into his medication, he said the sciatic pain in his lower back was so bad that "if it were acceptable, I would take myself out. I know this is only the second day, but how long do you think it will take before I feel some relief?" My heart broke for him, realizing how desperately he wanted to get out of this unbearable season of his life.

I said, "I know you'll start feeling better in a couple of days. So, hang in there a little while longer. Stick with the plan, and you'll experience a change soon."

Whenever a patient hints at suicide, I open a conversation.

I want to know how much they've thought about ending their lives, have they spoken with anyone else, have they written notes, do they know how they would go about it, and do they have the means? Then I make a verbal contract with them, reminding them of our partnership in treating their specific issues. I ask them to promise me and give me their word they'll continue with the plan we've agreed on to completion.

Peter gave me his word. "Yes, I will, and thank you, Doctor."

"Thank you," I said. "It's really important to me to see you come through this. We'll talk again at your two-week follow-up."

Two days later, Peter called and told me he was a different person from the one I spoke with in our last conversation.

His next appointment was where he held his MRIs in front of my face to prove his pain was real. Thankfully, we had a real solution.

A Personal, Mind-boggling Breakthrough

Boarding a plane to Chicago was exciting for several reasons.

First, I needed a break from the unrelenting demands of my practice and was looking forward to some much-needed alone time. Secondly, I enjoy traveling and the experience of different places and the various local cuisines.

Having lived in New York and Los Angeles, I was eager to see the renowned architecture of the "windy city" and experience its unique taste sensations. Third, I would be hearing from various specialists in the field of psychotropic medications, which would feed my desire to learn as much as I could about new ways to best treat my patients. So finally arriving in my hotel room was exhilarating, knowing I was going to enjoy every minute of this mini vacation.

The next morning, looking over the weekend agenda, I realized what an incredible opportunity this was going to be. The conference made history. It was the first time a pharmaceutical company introduced a medication remedy for bipolar disorder to primary care physicians. The audience for the lecture was mostly psychiatrists—I was one of a few family doctors invited. The pharmaceutical company considered us "thought leaders" in our profession, so we'd been handpicked.

The primary emphasis of the conference was to provide us with training to communicate with our colleagues the value of the new medications soon to hit the market for treating mood disorders. Our benefit was being exposed to innovative information from some of the top minds in the field. I was fascinated learning about the variety of bipolar disorders, a subject prior to the conference hadn't interested me much.

Most of my colleagues were familiar with the traditional definition of what was originally called manic depression but is now known as bipolar disorder. Manic referred to the "mania" of a highly activated brain, producing over-excited states that could cross the line into delusion and psychosis. The depression side is exactly what one would expect with typical unipolar depression; an unexplainable sadness or sense of hopelessness that is usually worse than those who suffer with the more common unipolar disorder. Bipolar refers to the two poles of mania and depression and the fact that the patient can shift—often quickly, erratically, and radically—from one pole to the other.

Most patients' current symptoms are subtle and often overlooked not only by family physicians but by many specialists.

Unfortunately, little has changed over the last two to three decades for primary care providers and psychiatrists. It's still true most cases of bipolar disorder go undiagnosed.

Since I had not expected how riveting the lectures would be, I showed up to the auditorium without a notepad, which I usually carried. Frantically I looked for something to write on and found a few loose sheets nearby.

Later, going over the binder the company had provided for the conference, I found the speaker's notes and photographs of the slides the presenters had used in their lectures. They'd provided clinical information regarding a new medication—Zyprexa.

The speakers delivered these priceless insights into the human brain, how different things can go wrong in it, and how many of those disorders can be corrected by advances in medicine.

Learning that bipolar disorders were most often misdiagnosed was a stunning revelation. I hadn't come across such information in any medical journals or psychiatric textbooks.

During the weekend I gained many other valuable insights. I learned there wasn't one specific version of bipolar disorder, but it could present different degrees of severity with greater or lesser debilitating effects. This explained why bipolar patients who didn't experience the mania side of their conditions didn't respond adequately to the usual standard or more modern antidepressants, the dynamic duo.

Some patients got worse when treated with antidepressants. Some won't see the profound significance of such a finding, but for me, it was like the announcement of a revolution in the science of healthcare.

On my flight home, I organized the chicken scratch of my notes into a readable outline. A large body of information grew and developed into the advances I made in my practice. As I pored over the new insights, I noted the names and faces of patient after patient who might benefit from new applications of informed use of different medications.

Another new available tool was Zyprexa, markedly more beneficial for patients whose bipolar disorder, depression, or anxiety wasn't responsive to antidepressants.

It's difficult to put into words the pleasure and satisfaction of realizing positive changes to my patients' lives once we begin working with medications—and combinations of medications—better suited to resolving their physical and psychological symptoms. Those feelings persist because the same improvements keep happening.

Two More Patients and Two More Breakthrough Insights

One of the first patients I wanted to see upon returning home from the conference was Armando, someone whom

I'd been treating for a year. I had prescribed the original dynamic duo of Effexor XR and Wellbutrin XL, resulting in his feeling better than he had in the previous twenty years. Not only were his depression and anxiety greatly reduced, but he experienced significant relief from his chronic upper and lower back pain—this coming after he'd seen a boatload of doctors without any improvement. However, in my opinion his progress was only a fifty-percent improvement. I always looked for the next step toward one hundred percent. I was more persistent in pushing for better results than my patients.

Armando still suffered insomnia, an unhealthy low weight due to his loss of appetite, and lingering depression.

After reviewing his medical history, I found no indications of mania, paranoia, bipolar 1 disorder, or the hypomania of bipolar 2 disorder. Based on what I learned from the clinical psychiatrists at the conference, I had a new perspective that made me rethink his diagnosis, which indicated bipolar depression rather than traditional unipolar depression or the "classic" bipolar one or two disorder. Previously, I believed his depression was treatment resistant, which has been a diagnosis physicians gratuitously applied to many patients who didn't respond adequately to the usual medications. After learning about Zyprexa, I added a new tonic in my "doctor's bag".[7]

The tragedy of schizophrenia and bipolar disorder is patients being driven to mental breaks with reality, referred to as psychosis. Sufferers may experience visual or auditory hallucinations, paranoia, and a radical disconnect with the real world. They sometimes pose the potential to harm themselves or others.

---

[7]This class of medications are dopamine antagonists, which slow down and suppress dopamine. They have positive effects on serotonin and often other neurochemicals. Wellbutrin has the opposite effect of boosting dopamine. I often combine them.

Zyprexa was developed as an antipsychotic medication to support such mental breaks. Prior to the conference, the possibility of treating depression or the variations of bipolar disorder with an antipsychotic medication hadn't occurred to me. Most patients with bipolar disorder don't suffer manic or psychotic episodes as much as those with depression. At the time, treating depression with Zyprexa was an "off label" use. Off label means information and indications that are not formally written in language allowed by the federal government, in particular the FDA.

Zyprexa label said nothing about using it to treat depression. In some instances, "off label" is another way of saying "cutting-edge" for the potential benefits. The FDA and federal government are not innovative thinkers, and we shouldn't take their medical advice.

I remember thinking, "No wonder patients like Armando appear to be treatment resistant. Their diagnosis was incomplete, making their treatment incomplete, as well." Most practitioners weren't (and many still aren't) aware of a better way to diagnose and treat really tough cases. My goal is to illuminate this ignorance by writing this book and others.

Before attending the life changing conference, I probably would've taken the same course as many of my colleagues. But I had a strong conviction there had to be a better way to realize improvement than we'd believed.

I was amazed as anyone at the results of combining Zyprexa (a dopamine antagonist) with the dynamic duo of Effexor XR and Wellbutrin XL. By addressing Armando's severe depression with the "antipsychotic"—which acted as a mood stabilizer—we witnessed a giant leap in improvement of his anxiety, depression, sleep patterns, and pain reduction.

Zyprexa became another well-fitting puzzle piece. Within two weeks leading up to his follow-up, adding a low dose of Zyprexa brought Armando to the goal he hoped for but had seemed unattainable. He enjoyed better and more refreshing sleep, his depression resolved, he rediscovered food, and regained much-needed weight.

Two months after the new treatment plan, while I was on the phone with one of my children, my assistant walked into my office and placed a handwritten letter on my desk.

After finishing the call, I picked up the letter, written in Spanish and broken English. It was from Armando's wife, Maria, sincerely expressing her gratitude. I was deeply moved.

Although we had never met, she poured her heart out to me about the man she married, who'd disappeared. He suddenly returned to her. Armando, who she'd nicknamed Manny in high school, was happy again, free of his horrendous pain.

She was shocked when he asked to cook her homemade enchiladas, carnitas, and posole, that she had to ask him to repeat what he'd said. Even then, her first thought was he must have been joking. Maria obliged him by hosting a big family feast featuring her amazing homemade Mexican food. She was offering prayers of thanks to God every day for bringing me into Armando's life, restoring their marriage and his relationship with their children.

Her joy in Armando's improvement and deep gratitude to me brought tears to my eyes. I realized what she described was the recovery of three of the most important aspects of our human experience—our families, our close friends, and, of course, authentic Mexican soul food, which my family often enjoys thanks to my wife. When I came home that day, I greeted my wife Denise with a big hug and kiss. I was feeling the same sense of gratitude and love for my wife, family, and home that Maria was experiencing with Manny and her family.

Like many doctors, I forget we're not only helping the patients we see, but we're making profound differences in the lives of those closest to them. Maria's letter was an instance of joy that comes in my profession when we walk side by side with our patients—that is, until they improve to the point where they are no longer dependent on us. Maria's was not the last letter I received where someone wanted to express gratitude or report their life's positive changes, nor was it the last time I felt overwhelmed and humbled by the depth of their appreciation. Some letters, emails, and phone calls have come from patients. Others arrive from family members, distant relatives, friends, and neighbors.

I have sometimes asked, "Why me, given all the professional doctors in the world?"

Then I remember the risks I took, the hours I poured into research, the sense of clarity I worked reaching, and my vulnerability in trying something new. At the same time, I acknowledge the rational course I've taken, resulting in handcrafted and individualized recipes of a variety of Corona Cocktails designed to achieve optimal results.

GABA-DABA-DOO!

Then there was Tessa, Contessa's nickname. For years she'd struggled with depression—and kept losing. Her loneliness and sadness began after she arrived in the United States from the Ivory Coast, having left her family to begin a new career. Eventually her fiancé was supposed to join her, but his plans had been delayed and she felt abandoned. Unable to overcome her heartache, she sank into worsening depression.

Once she recognized the seriousness of her mental state, she sought the help of physicians who had at various times prescribed Prozac, Zoloft, Lexapro, and Effexor XR, without producing any noticeable improvement. Her depression persisted and medical intervention failed her. Tessa descended into hopelessness with additional symptoms of fatigue, apathy, lack of motivation, and persistent headaches. When her conditions interfered with work, the added stress intensified her symptoms. Tessa's intuition told her she was getting worse with each medication, so she stopped them.

When we met, it was obvious that this thirty-eight-year-old woman had been ill for a good while. She spoke softly and appeared to carry the weight of the world on her shoulders. Her lethargy was also clear, and it pained me to see her so desperate to get out of the pit she was in, fearing nothing would change. I imagined how wonderful it'd be seeing her smile. I bet she'd do well experiencing a dopamine surge, so I gave her a prescription for Wellbutrin XL to get her body and mind moving in a positive direction.

I did not wait a full week to check in with her to see how she was doing. I instructed her if she felt the Wellbutrin was not helping, to stop taking it and call the office right away.

Two weeks later her depression had lessened, she had more energy, and she was interested in returning to some activities she'd previously enjoyed.

However, she'd been more irritable, wasn't sleeping well, and had a horrible sense of dread.

Each symptom suggested that she suffered with bipolar depression. If what she'd suffered was unipolar depression, the Wellbutrin would have been more effective.

A new mood stabilizer, another dopamine antagonist, had recently hit the market. It could be the answer.

I gave her samples of Abilify, and she gave me a half-mast smile. In her beautiful accent, she said, "Thank you, Doctor Paul."

I suggested she start thinking of getting back to more of the activities she used to enjoy.

Tessa surprised all of us in the office when she dropped in the following week without an appointment. After waiting patiently to grab a quick moment with me, she explained her visit was because she wanted me to know how much better she was feeling. What we noticed about her, and later remarked on, was how lovely her teeth appeared when she smiled.

I hadn't realized during her initial visit how tall she was. Her posture had been hunched forward and drooping.

Her upright spine and lifted chin complimented her stature. Abilify had done its job, balancing her mood by balancing dopamine in a different but complementary and symbiotic fashion with Wellbutrin XL, balancing dopamine 24/7.

At her following appointment, we reviewed her remaining health concerns. "I've always been self-conscious about my weight and I'm still having nagging migraine headaches," she said. "Is there some type of medicine to help with these issues?"

I said, "Yes, in fact there is a medication that can help. It is called Topamax, and it works on both of those issues."

Tessa looked at me as if I was a magician and said, "Really Dr. Paul? Are you serious or are you joking with me? Are you saying you have one pill that can help me lose weight and get rid of my headaches?"

She left the office with samples in hand.

My intention was to give Tessa good reason to hope for a positive outcome, without offering any guarantees. There's no magic bullet that produces the same effect for everyone—no "one size fits all." This time, about three weeks passed before we met again. This may be getting old for you—it never gets old for me—but Tessa's improvement was remarkable. She still had some way to go with her weight but was off to a good start. Rapid weight loss is never something we push. For one reason, it's not healthy to lose too much too fast. Another reason is rapid weight loss generally occurs as a result of an extreme diet, so once the period of dieting has ended, the weight is regained.

Gradual weight loss requires a lifestyle change, one that can hopefully be supported by breaking unhealthy habits and developing good habits. An improved mood can help motivate lifestyle changes and, in time, the lifestyle changes can lead to improvement in one's mood. She'd stopped having the migraine headaches that'd temporarily debilitated her at times.

Tessa's face glowed as she threw herself into my arms similar to the way you see loved ones greeted by family when they arrive in an airport. She exclaimed, "You, my dear, are a Godsend. If someone had told me a couple of months ago that I would feel this good, I would have thought they'd lost their mind. I didn't think it was possible to feel this great again, but my whole life has utterly changed thanks to you and your care. You knew exactly what I needed. In fact, my fiancé was speechless when he arrived at the airport and saw me for the first time in six months. I had no idea how much he had been affected by my unhappiness. He never complained about it or my weight for that matter, but he was happy for me."

Although I was happy to see Tessa doing so well, I asked myself, "Can she do better?"

I thought there was further benefit in Topamax, so I titrated her to a higher dose and scheduled an appointment for a month later.

When she returned, the gains were confirmed in what she shared of her photography and oil painting that'd resurfaced as a result of how well she felt in this season of her life.

The fourth neurochemical of the Fantastic Four is GABA (gamma aminobutyric acid). When balancing GABA and glutamate, along with making sure that the other three (or one or two of them depending on the individual) are accounted for, this can lead to full remission, which means complete improvement by optimally balancing the mind and body. The mission of the fantastic four is to come to save the day.

FUTURE BREAKTHROUGHS

This is by no means the last chapter of the story. There are insights yet to come.

Research is probing ever deeper into the chemistry of the brain to discover the optimal conditions for mental health. Pharmaceutical companies are bringing more medications to physicians and other prescribers while learning the art of fine-tuning their effects.

In life, one never quite knows the twists and turns that will occur or whether the next moment will bring a wonderful gift or a drastic failure despite all the hard work and investment of time and energy.

Through it all my patients keep me going and pushing through those doors into the unknown for the potential reward that awaits us. Overall, I see a bright future for people who we were unable to help only a few decades ago.

As an aside, it took a total of four years to write the first book and then a total of twelve years to finish my trilogy, which ended up weighing in at a whopping 1,200 pages. I've completed writing my fourth and fifth books. Book 4 is *The Corona Protocol Prescriber's Guides* and Book 5 is *The Corona Protocol: 3 Secrets to Success*. These are textbooks and training manuals prepared for doctors.

I'm preparing a teaching course on The Corona Protocol geared for clinicians, especially primary care providers such as family practitioners, pediatricians, internal medicine specialists, physician's assistants, and nurse practitioners. My hope is there'll be a number of psychiatrists interested in learning new methods.

After finishing the training manuals, it's taken me four years to complete my sixth book—the one you're reading.

PART SIX

Horrific Adversity and Awesome Reward Metamorphosis of My Practice at the Turn of the Millennium

In the previous chapters I introduced you to some of my cherished patients, attempting to let you see just enough of them to appreciate what wonderful people they are, the misery that had overtaken their lives, and the joy they have experienced in getting their lives back and recovering the joy of their youth. In this chapter I'm going to introduce you to one more person and provide much more detail regarding his descent into suffering. In fact, with this one person I am going to break the rules by exposing the real person behind the story. By the end of this chapter, you'll understand my reasons for wanting you to feel like you know him personally.

Remember a time in your life when you were pulled in many directions and felt obligated to accomplish every demand, but you ran yourself into the ground? We want to manage all our responsibilities and we know we could do it if only they came to us one at a time. But taking on too much at once and trying to do all of it on our own we exhaust our resources of physical, mental, and emotional energy. And if we work halfway through sleepless nights for five or six days we still run out of time. It is likely that either you or others you know practically kill themselves trying to do it all.

CHARLES

About six feet and four inches tall with a sturdy frame, Charles entered his marriage and career believing he could carry the weight of the world. If all of us at times fall prey to the temptation of taking on too much at once, for Charles overdoing it had become a lifestyle. He was in one of those professions requiring constant activity, which took twelve to fourteen hours a day, including Saturdays. After he learned the ropes, he opened his own office, which created a new set of obligations. If he was not spending time with clients, he would have a mountain of paperwork. He spent most Sundays preparing himself for the coming week.

Alongside his standard office hours, Charles had developed products that were relatively new and in high demand. His clients became his first customers and their referrals to others produced more customers so that Charles, while keeping pace with his regular office hours, was now servicing new customers for his products as well. Charles was fortunate to have a wife who understood the demands on his time and applauded the rapid growth of his business.

In time, she became worried he was not spending enough time with their children, who at ten and eight years old, were becoming aware of how rare it was to have a meaningful conversation with their dad.

Having become a workaholic, Charles did his best to create time for his children, which meant carving out time when he was at home. Unfortunately, he was unable to squeeze attending school functions and special events into his schedule.

When he had to tell his wife that it would be impossible for him to be present that afternoon for his daughter's performance at a school, she shared her resentment that'd been building because he'd let work come before his family and practically blotted them out.

Over the ensuing months, it was a complaint she'd not allow him to forget. He knew she was right, but when he took steps to reduce his workload, it only amplified the situation.

Charles increased his office staff and hired four others trained in his field to work alongside him. They became senior associates, whom he hoped to one day make full partners. He assumed that they could take on the responsibility of servicing the company's clients while he spent much of his time addressing the growing demand for his new products. But instead of giving him more free time he now had the added responsibilities of managing an office staff and the pressure of increased expenses.

Perhaps things would have smoothed out in time, but Charles found many of his clients were unhappy when they were shuffled off to his associates. He was hearing client comments about not being able to see the boss, and in some cases, they were dissatisfied with the care given by his associates.

After a while he was taking the blame and many clients decided to abandon him and seek out his competitors. Charles took it personally because, having worked hard for their patronage for fifteen years, he always felt a strong bond with his clients, even if they couldn't meet as often as they would have liked.

Upset over this loss, Charles reached out to his former clients, sending over a thousand one-page personalized letters explaining the reason for the transition and apologized. An emotional disruption was added to his level of stress. Although he had always enjoyed his work and found being busy satisfying, his stress was increasing, and he couldn't carry it on his own.

He'd devised a strategy that backfired. It resulted in him spending even less time with his wife and children.

Positive stress can cause as much wear and tear to the nervous system as negative stress. In his early forties and seemingly invincible, Charles was unaware of the toll good stress can take and was unaware of his dwindling resources.

The Proverbial Hammer Falls

Long-time customers weren't the only losses Charles sustained. His business, like many others during those years of rapid growth, thrived until the nation's economy turned from boom to bust.

The timing couldn't have been worse. While Charles' side business had been expanding, his two junior associates did not have enough work to fill their days. The two senior associates who were busy jumped ship and moved to a neighboring town. Pouring salt in the wound he felt over their departure, they took half of the clients of his business with them. The two junior associates did not have enough business, and also left. He had a 4,000 ft^2 office, staff, expensive equipment, and overhead to cover. The damage done by his former associates was devastating and irreversible.

Charles felt overwhelmed and defeated. Unable to sleep, he turned his attention towards documenting what he learned in developing his side business and organized that information into a book. Sitting at his computer in the silence hanging over his home as his family slept was like therapy, giving him a sense of calm and a sense of calling and purpose, making up for his sleep loss.

The enthusiastic response to the product line he developed confirmed that many people, perhaps millions, could benefit from what he had learned. If he could just get the word out, he knew it would spread and catch on quickly so others could enter the new field and reproduce his work.

Still supportive, his wife was becoming increasingly concerned about his health and mental status, wondering how long he could bear the surplus stress. His children understood their dad was a hard worker with too much to do, but knew he loved them beyond words.

The economic downturn turned into a serious recession, challenging his business and those of many Americans.

The day came when Charles couldn't make payroll and reneged on his lease. Becoming more devoted to writing, he became frenetic in his eagerness to finish his book, which he managed to do despite the situation.

He had dreamed of being an author, and he was determined to make that happen but that was his only silver lining because his first business failed financially, and Charles was faced with bankruptcy.

Circumstances became grim for him and his wife. Both their cars were repossessed, and they barely managed to hang on to their home. To this day, Charles is grateful he never lost his family, and wonders how his wife remained loving and devoted. The worst was yet to come.

Charles was getting less and less sleep and, in fact, went for several consecutive days with no sleep. He found it impossible to shut his brain off, worrying about how they would dig themselves out of the hole they were in, or soothing himself with thoughts about his book reaching a tipping point and causing an avalanche benefitting millions of people. He felt he was being crushed by the weight of the world without a safety net to support him and his family, and without a clear plan on how to go forward. His once ideal existence had become a living nightmare as he contemplated all the people he'd failed.

Charles' whole life was collapsing. He needed something big to happen in order to get his life back on track.

Plagued by spiraling thoughts, he believed in his vision of what needed to be done, and of the impossibility of making it happen on his own. But with every door closing, he had no choice but to pursue his dream. However, a dream can be a wispy and unreal thing to rely on when it comes to paying a mortgage and providing for a family.

One Sunday, things changed. Rather than feeling beaten down, Charles felt energized. He saw straight into the heart of his most serious concerns with perfect clarity. The value of his research discoveries and new products took on a greater meaning than ever before. He knew it'd gain worldwide attention. Consumed with writing and taking pride in his ability to work on it without needing to waste time on sleep, the problem was all his great strength, insight and understanding was in his head, not in the real world.

Charles Was Having a Nervous Breakdown

The first person to notice he'd swung outside his characteristic calm behavior was his wife. He was yelling loud enough to get the attention of the neighbors, and his diatribe made no sense. Unable to calm him or reason with him, Charles' wife called their pastor and asked if he could come over and get through to him.

She knew Charles had profound respect for him. If he was going to listen to anyone, it'd be their pastor. Within twenty minutes of his arrival, it was obvious that, try as he might, there was nothing he could do for Charles. So, she made the difficult call to the sheriff's office and paramedics.

It's a sad fact most law enforcement officers receive little training dealing with mental disorders or those with disabilities. People on the autism spectrum, Tourette's syndrome, and hearing-impaired individuals have been mistreated and unnecessarily roughed up by police officers who mistook their behavior, assuming they were being uncooperative, combative, or threatening.

The sheriffs who arrived at Charles' home asked his wife if her husband been using drugs. "No," she said.

That being their primary concern, they weren't interested in hearing about the stress he'd been under, his sleeplessness, or any other factor that'd suggest another explanation for his bizarre behavior.

Fortunately, there are some bright people in law enforcement who educate themselves about mental disorders, and many others who are simply good people willing to give troublemakers the benefit of the doubt, seeing and speaking with them prior to judging them.

Those sheriffs weren't of either of those categories. They were with Charles for just a few minutes before determining he was whacked out on drugs. They didn't consider the possibility of acute mania. In order to subdue him, they both tasered him.

Police know tasers are ineffective on a drug user high on PCP or methamphetamines. When shot, some offenders have pulled the prongs out and continued trying to escape and remained combative.

When Charles was hit with the taser, he fell.

Within seconds, he was yelling again. In his right mind, he never would've foolishly shouted "Is that all you've got?"

The sheriffs felt certain he was high and tasered him again. The pastor tried intervening, going down on his knees next to Charles, begging him to be quiet and cooperate. But Charles was no longer capable of hearing anyone.

A sheriff yelled, "If you don't back away from the suspect, you'll get tasered, too."

By the sixth taser, the sheriffs were amused by how much Charles could withstand and still go on yelling.

They tasered him eight times.

Finally, paramedics arrived. Having a better idea of what Charles was experiencing, they sedated him and rushed him to a local hospital.

His wife and pastor were admitted to the emergency room.

They stood next to his bed and talked softly with him.

Charles appeared remorseful and apologetic and was unclear why he was there.

This was the beginning of the darkest season of his life.

He spent Christmas in the locked ward of a special care hospital. Charles had the best possible doctor attending him: a brilliant psychiatrist who was a good and compassionate man who cared for him as a person. Charles remained sad and desolate. Discouraged, he found it difficult to believe it was in his nature to fall apart. Despite all the business setbacks and unrelenting stress he'd endured over many years, nothing similar had ever happened.

Charles ached for his family and the time he missed not being able to spend the holidays with them. It was the one season he'd shut down his office and celebrate. The memories of them being together, special meals, the fun and laughter all intensified his loneliness.

But Charles was a fighter. He was going to get all the possible information about his condition and what had happened. He'd get back on his feet and continue on his mission and passion. He believed he was on the verge of a major breakthrough.

At first, he balked at how much time he'd remain hospitalized. He hoped he'd be released after his first week once his caseworker saw how good he was doing.

Learning it'd be another few weeks, he became agitated.

Nevertheless, he realized he needed the rest and it felt good allowing others to care for him.

He left the hospital fully recovered—a new man. The stay worked to his advantage when he returned to his life's challenges. But all was not perfect. There was more adversity to come.

The Road Back

Today, Charles looks back on his surreal experience. Rather than mourn, he gives thanks for all he's gained. His attending psychiatrist in the hospital told him he believed in him sincerely and prescribed medications, careful to give him the widest latitude to ensure his inventive and creative side.

Returning to work, he kept it simple. He decided to work alone and focus on developing his side business rather than return to the full range of services he'd previously offered, and to continue his writing.

One of the greatest gifts he received in recovery and rebuilding his business was learning the skill of how to balance his life. Charles was aware of the importance of listening to his body, his wife, and close friends.

He recognized when he needed to make time to play, read, and write in a balanced way. He exercised and spent quality time with his family, including his beloved cat Ella, a beautiful blue point Himalayan who lived 19 years.

His life became whole. It made an enormous difference for him and his loved ones.

A last piece of information regarding this patient ...

drum roll ...

I am Charles.

The story you've just read is mine.

Why tell my story in the third person? Reason number one is I choose to distance myself from the dark episode of my breakdown. I'm not that person who fell over the edge. Like many who live with bipolar disorder, the extreme mania was an aberration. It was the result of a severe, undiagnosed chemical imbalance due to stress, lack of sleep, and overwork.

Through rest, the care of a knowledgeable and well-trained physician, and the proper dose of the most effective medications, my condition was fully resolved. Since then, I haven't suffered a severe flareup or breakdown.

A second reason for hiding my identity was wanting to give you a sense of standing next to me, seeing this patient's suffering. I felt it was important to see him objectively and hopefully feel empathy for him. I think you would have read the story differently if you knew it was an autobiography.

The final reason was so you might appreciate my knowing bipolar disorder from the inside. In fact, I know the most painful and embarrassing possibilities of this disorder—something not every bipolar patient lives through.

Only 10% of bipolar patients experience true mania. I'm driven to stop it from happening to anyone else. I'm compelled to relieve people suffering depression, eating disorders, or obsessive-compulsive behavior. My empathy isn't just pity because I truly identify with my patients. I know the hell a mood disorder brings, but also the wonderful experience of a life in which passion and joy are recovered after the disorder is resolved.

* * *

Regarding the book I mentioned in my narrative was the first of a three-book series entitled *Healing the Mind and Body: The Trilogy,* which took me 12 years to complete and weighs in at 1,200 pages. I didn't realize I was writing three books. Once I put down what I learned and developed, I had to cut off the first book and divide the material into two books.

The second book was too lengthy for a single volume and a third book was necessary to complete the basic survey of symptomology: a detailed explanation of neurochemical factors, and an extensive list of all the psychotropic medications for resolving mood and physical disorders.

My first audience were family practice physicians like me, so I also provided recommendations for creating a safe environment for patients through building a partnership with them and working up an extensive family and medical history. Such information would be helpful for patients, giving them an understanding and an inside look into the mindset of the provider, and how and why we make the decisions. I kept writing.

Books four and five are small textbooks used as training manuals. I want as many family physicians, psychiatrists, and other prescribers as possible to learn about The Corona Protocol. For that, I've developed a certification training program walking them through the information and treatment process.

The sixth book is the one that you're reading now.

The colleagues and associates in the narrative included family doctors, all four of whom I'd hired to join me right out of residency training. Employees were our medical assistants, receptionists, billing, office manager, and a filer. I've always wanted to influence other doctors by providing a positive example, however, in truth, I was destined to be a solo practitioner.

It became obvious I function best in my own space and time. I've been trained and licensed to treat patients, not to run a business or manage a staff.

At the same time, teaching and training other physicians and specialists brings me as much joy as treating my own patients, knowing I'm equipping others to extend this important work to other patients.

When referring to "specialty products and services," it meant the psychotropic medications and the importance of varying doses of different medications, often low doses of an array of medications with different modes of action combined, individualized to the needs of each patient. I combine them in unique ways for "off label" applications, translating to the most innovative science, which leads to dramatic results.

It's important to master the art and science of the rational poly-pharmaceutical approach to achieve optimum mind-body health. Charles' business was my medical "practice"—I like to say I keep practicing until I get it right.

Regarding the clients and the sadness Charles felt in losing many of them, I was describing my own pain when patients left our office for another doctor because I was unable to fit everyone into my schedule.

Since I knew of no one else offering the same kind of help, I felt burdened and energized by the difficult responsibility to prepare, meet demand, and share my insights and results.

The work I've devoted to The Corona Protocol wasn't what I thought I'd be doing when I graduated from medical school. It's since occupied my practice for over thirty years—an arduous endeavor not for the faint of heart—but giving up on my vision never occurred to me.

I never considered my work a day job where I'd clock out at five o'clock. My calling was developed over 50,000[8] hours of clinical practice, entailing over 150,000 office visits.

It took all I had to keep up; the toll on my mind and body was enormous.

---

[8]In Malcolm Gladwell's book *The Outliers*, his research has shown it takes 10,000 hours to achieve mastery and expertise in a given field.

When my patient base shrunk, my assisting physicians left, too. Losing the group practice, followed by our financial distress and mounting stress—was more than I could handle.

I carried the overwhelming responsibility to the millions of people suffering needless misery that could be resolved by changing our perspective on how best to treat mind-body ailments.

I reached a point where my mind-chatter wouldn't shut off for a moment. Sleep eluded me. I theorized ways the nervous system might become imbalanced and how specific medications would work best in resolving neurochemical problems.

The pressure of sharing this information was immense, especially when realizing it was going to take so much time and energy to reach others through writing and lecturing. I knew it'd be more difficult than I imagined but felt there was no choice but to pursue and prove it. The weight of the world was on my shoulders. Not being Atlas, the strain broke me.

There is so much I could say about my wonderful family. My greatest joy comes from the time I spend with them. My wife Denise is an incredibly talented woman with a beautiful singing and acting voice and has been professionally involved in those fields. Being the daughter of a gourmet cook, she works magic in our kitchen. Part of our family tradition in November is preparing two to three hundred tamales (pork molé and green chili and cheese) to celebrate Christmas Eve.

Denise organizes an assembly line of family and close friends, each with a different task, starting with washing of the ojas (corn husks). That's my job, along with serving and partaking in whichever craft beer I have on tap. My Tiki Bar (man cave) in my back yard was built by my father Arthur (Art-Art!), an accomplished real estate developer. I make my special recipe of mixed berry margarita. A good friend nicknames them Dr. Happy margaritas.

Other duties include spreading the matzoh (or masa) on the ojas (corn husks). Denise stuffs and rolls each expertly,

286

handing them off to be hand counted and packaged for the freezer ... except for the ones that we eat after we are done for the day. We then come together for our annual Christmas Eve party for our family and close friends. She complements the tamales with her family recipe for Spanish rice and her own secret recipe for homemade salsa. Everyone raves.

After the meal, there's five large trays of delicious Dolce di Ricotta—mini ricotta cheese cookie cakes—that never last.

The tradition continued the year I was locked away in the hospital, bored and lonely. Denise remained my rock through it all. My heart longed for her. My son Logan and daughter Baylee turned ten and eight that year. I missed my dad, whose presence made Christmas a joy. To this day, I love and appreciate my family more than ever.

"Out of the frying pan!"

Leaving the hospital and reviving my practice felt more like an exciting prospect than going back to work. I found a small office space not far from our home. I'm within walking distance. I decided I'd be working alone with my awesome assistant in a small, comfortable office. My dream was to be a solo practitioner in private practice, and it was granted. I resumed meeting with patients, focusing my practice on mind-body treatment.

My new lifestyle was more balanced, allowing for more family time. Thanks to their loving support, I learned to discipline myself and add quality to my life. Gone were the days of working twelve to fourteen hours. I felt refreshed and made it to dinner each night. I was healthier and happier and took nothing for granted, savoring each precious moment.

Then the storm fronts moved in.

One afternoon, the wind was knocked out of me when I opened a letter from the CA Medical Board. They informed me that I was being placed on a five-year probation period for no other reason than I'd been hospitalized and treated for my breakdown. I appreciate the safeguards in place protecting patients from doctors who are unethical or incompetent, but I was not guilty of any wrongdoing, nor had any of my patients been endangered. I'd been cleared to return to work by the psychiatric team in the hospital, who also monitored my progress over the first few months while restarting my practice. My probation was cut back to three years for good behavior. My license wasn't restricted or suspended.

The probation had conditions. First, I had to take university level medical courses, which were easy to ace but stole a lot of time from my practice. I had to cover the significant expense of the classes and was charged tens of thousands of dollars by the medical board for administrative costs and fees for the probation officer whom I met with every three months. I had to find and hire another doctor to monitor my practice and review our charts. The monitor wrote an outstanding review of my record-keeping and patient care and the probation officer gave me an excellent rating in her report.

Having done my due diligence to the medical board, I asked for an early release from probation. This was a possibility after two years, providing all requirements were met. That's why my probation lasted three years rather than five. Having all of that behind me was a great relief. I had clear skies, a calm sea, and a strong wind filling my sails. My happiness was complete—for a few days.

At first, it was exciting to have a newspaper reporter call and request an interview. He seemed friendly enough and was asking all the right questions. It seemed like the sort of opportunity I'd been hoping for to publish my research.

His questions covered drug addiction, the high number of opiate overdoses, and my unique practice of treating mood disorders with psychotropic medications. He hid his intention to use his column to attack and discredit me. I naively walked into the line of fire which haunted me for several years.

Prior to the reporter's call, a young man had been brought to my office to be treated for his mood disorder, which led to his addiction to prescribed opiates and heroin. I'll refer to him as Toby. Sadly, he did not continue long enough to stick with the treatment plan. I wasn't his primary aid in working through his detox and recovery. He'd been referred by his psychologist to supplement his therapy.

Toby's diagnosis was bipolar disorder with comorbidity—he suffered from bouts of depression and anxiety. It was no wonder he'd been self-medicating. I prescribed an antidepressant and a mood stabilizer because they've proven effective in reducing the brain's craving for controlled substances. They also produce a sense of well-being. When a person has overloaded their brains with opiates, their bodies read the excess of pleasure chemicals and stop producing them.

For the first two to three months, they're not capable of positive feelings, although they can still experience "down" or depressive feelings. An antidepressant allows the addict to have some positive feelings and reduces the temptation to keep self-medicating.

My role in aiding this young man was balancing neurochemicals within his nervous system, achieving optimal results through mind-body harmony. This is a much better treatment program than prescribing methadone, which has serious side effects such as risking a lethal overdose.

After beginning treatment, a friend of Toby's who'd been battling cancer succumbed.

Grief over losing someone close is typically overwhelming and requires a long time to process, especially when that person is as young as Toby and his friend. For the addict, overwhelming feelings can appear impossible to endure. Having developed a habit of escaping difficult situations or feelings through drugs, it's not unusual to relapse when encountering one of life's most difficult challenges. On the day of his friend's funeral, Toby was found deceased from an overdose of opiates, indicated by paraphernalia found next to his body.

Hearing the report of Toby's death devastated me. I'd been convinced he'd succeed in his recovery. The therapist who referred Toby was someone I knew: our offices were in the same building. We felt I was the right physician to aid him. She and I agreed there'd been no indication of suicidal ideation, or his having a plan to end his life. When a young person dies, we cannot help but ask, "Why?"

It's typical to place responsibility on someone other than the child. Toby's mother wanted to blame me for writing out prescriptions for her son. Toby's psychologist was a friend of his mother and was able to assure her the medications weren't responsible for nor a factor in his overdose.

When the news reporter interviewed me, his questions had an edge I didn't expect. Looking back, I see that regardless of what I said, he hadn't come prepared to listen, but to twist my words, take snippets of a sentence here and there from my first book, and weave together a column that misrepresented me in every way. When he published his article a couple of days later, I was floored.

Near the front of Orange County's largest newspaper, he slandered me, and printed my office and my home addresses. He implied I was partly responsible for Toby's death, which he picked up from the mother's report without doing any follow-up with her, Toby's therapist, or any other professional qualified to confirm the validity of my actions.

The reporter took the opportunity to reveal my breakdown and hospitalization, using it as an attempt to demolish my credibility. These actions were deceitful, to say the least. He outright lied claiming I lost my medical license. It's never been suspended nor have any restrictions been placed on it.

The article was a few, lengthy paragraphs long. Lacking the integrity of a true investigative journalist and a writer's talent for delivering information through engaging and interesting prose, the reporter attempted to bolster a weak, poorly researched and written piece by stretching it out over several newspaper columns, using innuendos, leading questions, and twisted interpretations of issues and situations in which he obviously lacked any knowledge or understanding. I felt like someone had sucker-punched me. Denise grieved over the nonsense he wrote and wept as she read his column.

I asked myself, "How could a reporter, someone people depend on for careful investigation and exact information, be so completely bereft of integrity? And what motivated him to work this hard at defaming me?"

After several attempts to hold the newspaper's editors accountable for what they'd published, all they did was report a retraction of the false statement my medical license had been revoked. The retraction consisted of a small paragraph a person would have to search hard to find. I doubt that five percent of those who read the full article saw the retraction.

My first impulse was to launch a lawsuit against the reporter and the paper for libel and the damage done to my reputation. However, my patient load was increasing, and it seemed a better decision to focus on them rather than spend money and waste time going after the perpetrators. If ever there was a time I had to go deep into my heart and soul to find God's strength, this was it.

That reporter? He must feel he's found a formula that'll ensure him a readership by going after other professionals, slandering them, and damaging their reputations. He doesn't realize the number of people who won't get the help they need because his articles have persuaded them doctors aren't trustworthy. The truth is? I don't think he cares. Perhaps it was naive of me, until that article was published, to trust media sources as sources of unbiased information.

I realize what's said in an interview may be twisted to have the opposite meaning by clever editing by a devious reporter. A positive outcome? I've learned to be as transparent as possible in my writing, speaking, podcasts and interviews, sticking to the truth and living my beliefs as authentically as possible. I thank God the reporter's attempt to ruin me failed. Still, my heart aches for those who could've been helped had they not read or believed what he'd written.

A Reflective Pause

I'm going to digress and share some thoughts regarding the hard stuff. Making our way through one rough patch after another, my constant thought was, "There has to be a reason all this stuff's happening." I understand how important it is to believe the hard things serve a purpose.

In his autobiography, a well-known pastor wrote, "Everything's preparation for something else" or as Nietzsche said, "What does not kill me makes me stronger." Without knowing why so much adversity came our way, we kept our faith, trusting that one day its purpose would reveal itself. One day we'll be able to tell our story.

Feeling like the main character in a horror film, I had to make my way through dark passages cluttered with countless dangers, hidden until they jumped out. I learned to document everything—no one could make this stuff up.

You can't bottle and put a label on grace, but neither can we live without it. Grace explains why each time I fell, I was able to get back up and keep moving. I didn't have strength. I was given strength, courage, and compassion.

Another lesson I learned about adversity is that it drives our core virtues. We're easy prey for our ego-self and can fail to become fully human. It's typical of narcissists that their ego-self cuts off compassion and kindness. Given enough adversities, and they're intense enough, they'll devour every ounce of ego-self and its superficial pose.

The broken person, if forced to lean on others, learns the necessity of healthy relationships. To be fully human is to love and be loved.

Denise was my rock in remarkable ways during our darkest hours. The joy I've derived from Denise, my son Logan, my daughter Baylee, my father Arthur, and my friend Chuck, have supported me in many ways. I believe them when they say I've been a supporter and encourager for them, as well.

Shake, Rattle and Roll Over and Play Dead

In the worst moments of life, it's enough knowing just one thing for certain: my place in the world is at the side of others fostering their healing and restoring their lives.

There were two specific instances when I wondered if I'd ever dig myself out.

Marci

I was three years out from the newspaper article and five years out from probation. I was under a pile of rubble wondering if I'd ever see the light of day. A family physician referred Marci to me to decide whether there was a better way to treat her insomnia. She was taking strong medications not intended as a sleep aid.

A quiet woman, Marci's situation would be challenging but doable. Going over her medical history, I found a red flag.

I wouldn't normally recommend the type of medications she'd been prescribed because they can cause unpredictable, unwanted behavior. Patients may not know or remember they'd been sleepwalking and eating in the middle of the night. They're not getting the right kind of sleep[9], so they're still tired and groggy the next day. Besides the side effects, these medicines are addictive. Marci had been on these potent medications, but they weren't working.

If a patient agrees to the treatment recommended by a doctor, it is crucial they're compliant and follow the doctor's instructions exactly as given. Sometimes a patient, while listening to instructions, will nod their head and appear amenable, assuring their physician they understand and will stick to the program. The physician must win the patient's trust to inspire the necessary compliance.

Sometimes with new patients—and always with some patients—the doctor must work harder to win their trust, especially when it involves a new regimen.

---

[9]REM (Rapid Eye-Movement) sleep is necessary for the body and mind to rest enough to be refreshed and energized. There are sleep medicines that "knock a person out" while depriving them of dream states that help the brain to normalize itself and resolve stresses.

Despite my direct instructions, the hard fact is there'll be patients who, against orders, will continue to take medications they're told not to. They'll fail to tell their doctor or specialist.

Combining medications without knowing their potent effects or side effects can result in severe and lasting consequences, even death. Some patients may think taking a medication prescribed by their doctor for a physical condition such as diabetes will not be affected if they're prescribed a medication for an emotional disorder, but that's not the case.

All medications affect the functions of the nervous system. Many do not realize that when they choose to not follow their doctor's recommendations they are "playing doctor" and self-medicating. Doctors cannot violate their patients' free will, so it is always our hope they'll adhere to our directions and confer with us before making any changes. I was as clear as could be when I explained to Marci that under no condition could she continue to take any other sleep medication or tranquilizer while taking what I'd prescribed.

In Marci's case, insomnia was symptomatic of a larger problem in that she was bipolar. I recommended a medication that's proven to be effective for sleep as well as stabilizing mood. It is really good for tough insomnia, which is common in bi-polar disorder. She no longer needed the sleeping pills. Not combining them with any other medication was key.

I sometimes struggle with patients in which it seems we have established a good rapport and partnership in our one visit, but then leave the office and I never hear from them again. Later I may learn from another doctor or family member that the patient has chosen to revert to their old ways.

For instance, it's not at all unusual for a bi-polar patient who has enjoyed the boost in energy, motivation, productivity, and sheer excitement they experience in their manic state to discontinue their medication knowing that the mania will not last, and the crash afterwards can be quite severe.

I am assuming Marci decided she did not want to turn her energy level down to normal. She may not have realized that burning energy on the high octane of mania wouldn't result in her getting tired enough to fall asleep. That kind of activation during the day doesn't shut off at night. Many like Marci have been hyped up for so long, it feels normal. A change to a healthier state feels wrong or uncomfortable.

Two weeks after our appointment, I learned of Marci's tragic decision to go off her prescribed medication and return to her old routine. This decision resulted in a fatal accident. While driving, Marci ran into and killed a woman riding her bike. Her primary care physician said Marci had taken a sleeping pill before getting behind the wheel the morning of the accident. I cannot imagine what it'd be like to live with something like that for the rest of one's life.

The shocker came when a lawsuit was filed against Marci's primary physician and me. I did not see that coming. After all, how could we be at fault when we advised her against her actions? Marci was the one who chose to ignore our instructions and self-medicate. Who'd believe any doctor would prescribe a morning sleeping pill before driving—that would be more certain to cause an accident than drinking and driving.

The other doctor and I shared the same malpractice insurance company. We knew we were legitimate in our patient care and did everything by the book. We'd not been remiss in any obligation to the patient. The police report was clear, placing all the blame on the driver. Knowing the lawsuit was spurious, we were confident the insurance company's lawyers would go to the judge and get the case dismissed.

But that wasn't how it worked out. The insurance company worried that if the suit went to a jury trial, jurors would be sympathetic to the family of the woman who'd died and award them a great deal more money than if they could settle out of court. So, they agreed to a settlement of one million dollars from each of our policies, assuring us this was the best way to manage the situation. They explained a court trial would consume a lot of time, taking us away from our normal office hours. Wasn't that the reason we paid those premiums in the first place?

We agreed it wasn't practical to take two or three weeks off for a trial, so we took the deal. What the insurance company failed to tell us was that because they paid off the settlement, it'd be reported to the CA Medical Board.

The other family doctor, who'd initially prescribed the sleeping pill, was spared probation. I believe I was on their radar and was a target because I'd been on probation. I suspect some felt I was practicing psychiatry without the proper training and credentials. Sure enough, the Medical Board placed me on immediate probation—which meant a second 5-year period for me. Had the insurance company not persuaded us to settle, we most likely would have won the case, since there was no malpractice on our part. The possibility of probation wouldn't have come up. After thirty years of private practice, I'm still learning the legal and bureaucratic ins and outs of having a medical practice.

Margaret

Not long after this unhappiness with the situation Marci created and before the second probation, a woman living in Florida contacted me to ask if I would interview her online. She introduced herself and told me her name was Margaret. "My sister is one of your patients and we share the same diagnosis. My sister told me she had improved so much from your treatment, I was wondering if you could help me, too, from the other side of the country."

I agreed and had Margaret fill out the intake and evaluation forms and provide complete medical and family histories. I requested her medical records and a signed consent from her doctors so I could treat her as I would any new patient.

During our first visit, I spent an hour with her reviewing her history and putting together a plan of action. I began with the same medication, which I had so much success with treating Margaret's sister. I made fine adjustments according to specific items discussed in our interview.

Sure enough, Margaret responded favorably, feeling much better and experiencing a significant difference in physical functions and mood. We weaned her off a couple of sedating and potentially addictive and unnecessary medications.

But before her next follow-up appointment I received a phone call from the medical director of her clinic where she'd been receiving treatment. He informed me he'd not given his personal consent for me to treat Margaret. I explained the attending physician had given his consent, as had the patient, who was already reporting improvement. Although patient consent was all that was needed technically, the permission from her attending physician is always an ethical concern.

298

My response was ignored. He accused me of practicing medicine in Florida without a state license and he intended to report me to the California State Medical Board. I countered with the fact that my care for Margaret was within the purview of practice as with any other physicians who work with patients out of state, and that to prescribe non-addictive psychotropic medications doesn't violate any state or federal laws.

I'd never met or heard of this man, so I'm not in a position to make judgments. The open hostility and combative response, as well as his general attitude and tone reminded me of an arrogant physician who felt slighted someone else was able to achieve positive results that he and his clinic failed to achieve.

I wish those factors made a difference when an accusation is delivered to the Medical Board. They do not because the Board is bound by their own rules to investigate any accusation and act, regardless of who files it. The case came on the heels of Marci's lawsuit and produced a plethora of miserable repercussions.

* * *

Being on probation means the Medical Board is alert to and actively looking for other evidence the doctor under investigation is guilty of malpractice, incompetence, fraud, inadequate record-keeping, any type of abuse, or many other violations that can justify suspending or revoking his or her license to practice medicine. When my name came up again, the Medical Board immediately took notice.

I went to work at once to stave off the worst possible consequences. As soon as the Board requested my medical records for both Marci and Margaret, I sent them everything I'd compiled. I offered them explanations for every step I took and made myself available for any interviews they wanted.

The entire time the Medical Board reviews a case can be an unnerving and anxiety ridden period for the person under investigation. Fortunately, I was in good physical and mental health, and I was able to remain calm knowing I'd not done anything deserving suspension or censure.

To cut to the chase, for the second time in five years, I was placed on probation. The fees, penalties, and administrative costs tripled, as were the number of required medical courses. Once again, I had to pay for another doctor to watch me and meet monthly to discuss my practice and quarterly to go over charts. I had to pay for the probation officer to meet with me quarterly, combined with exorbitant fees and associated administrative costs.

I was scheduled for an evaluation by a team of psychiatrists for detailed testing. I suspected they were concerned or curious about a family doctor who'd apparently practiced full-time psychiatry for almost twenty years—something unheard of in their field.

Prior to the week of intensive evaluation, I was notified that if the team of psychiatrists weren't convinced, I was qualified to care for patients in the way I'd been treating them with mood-stabilizing medications, I'd have to complete a three-year residency training program. I was in shock. During that time, I would have had to stop giving my patients the care they'd come to rely on. I would have to close my practice, complete the studies, and start over. This was not good news for my patients or me.

The Medical Board's decision to have me evaluated by a team of psychiatrists rather than family doctors, which was what my education prepared me for and was the basis of my practice, was a revelation to me as to their intentions—and worked to my advantage.

Psychiatrists must have a medical license and family physicians must have some training in psychiatry to complete a well-rounded education. In the eyes of the Medical Board, I'd been doing the work of a psychiatrist. They wanted to decide whether I met the qualifications and criteria to be engaged in that field. I cannot remember the exact number of psychiatrists that interviewed me over the course of that entire week, but it dragged on slowly as I met with one esteemed professional after another. Dozens of my charts and clinical case studies were reviewed and evaluated. I was required to make rounds providing psychiatric inpatient, outpatient, and emergency room care under supervision, supplying reports on the patients I treated.

During those exhausting interviews, more than one psychiatrist asked me why I was on probation and what I was doing there. Based on the information they'd received regarding Marci's lawsuit and the medical director who complained about my treatment of Margaret, investigation into my qualifications didn't make sense to them. They treated me as a peer.

To my great relief, each professional was sympathetic to my situation and showed me kindness, going as far as complimenting my work throughout that week. Several team members expressed how impressed they were with my approach, saying they enjoyed hearing about it and used words like "refreshing" and "innovative."

I felt encouraged but will admit it was stressful being subjected to so much questioning and scrutiny. Regardless, it always gave me pleasure to explain how I developed my course of treatment. Having longed for the opportunity to pass on my discoveries to other professionals, I finally had the opportunity to do so with people who had the training to understand, appreciate, and listen carefully to what I had to say.

They recognized my ease in going over my charts and presenting my cases; an ease that comes with a thorough knowledge of the subject. Their response was to a colleague, not as a wrongdoer who deserved probation, strapped with the enormous expenses of the process.

Several commiserated, letting me know they felt it was unfair for me to endure what I was going through. As much as I dreaded going into it, the experience turned out to be a week to remember. If nothing else, it guaranteed my status among psychiatrists as one of them, rather than an outsider encroaching on their field.

One other outcome of this unexpected and expensive ordeal came from a requirement placed on me by the team of psychiatrists. I had to take the psychiatric board exam in order to complete their evaluation. I took every spare minute to study for the exam, read psychiatric textbooks, and tried my best to prepare however I could.

I passed with flying colors. The significance of this accomplishment is that this is the exam every psychiatrist must pass to be board certified.

I was subjected to a challenging cognitive exam. Thankfully, I passed that, as well as all the challenges they threw at me. They concluded I was fully qualified to continue the work that'd been so important to me and my patients for years. This was music to my ears. I received an education, commendation, and an endorsement that strangely, as difficult as it was, proved worth the price paid.

EPILOGUE

When I began writing this series of books, I was determined to open my heart and tell the entire story of my own experience of bipolar disorder and the hardship it created for my family. Having revealed some of my personal struggles, I want to share another side of my inner life; something that's been the positive energy enabling me to do better for more people than I'd ever dreamed.

By now you know I am not satisfied if the only gains my patients experience are that their lives are tolerable or more manageable. Even if some patients are content to reach those stages, I want more for them. My goal is to restore their passion for life and rediscover the brightest days of their youth. Passion, like any emotion, is not easy to define. It is easier to talk about the ways our emotions feel or affect us. They bring tears to our eyes or a smile to our lips; they cause us to tighten our jaws and clench our fists; they have us pacing the floor or racing to get somewhere.

When we talk about having a passion for something, we are referring to a motivating emotion that inspires, enlivens, and drives us. It can be a conviction that there is an important task to be performed, and we can perform it. Passion is a mental force that makes a person jump out of bed in the morning eager to dive into the new day. When our passion is directed to a certain project, our attention is focused, our hands are busy, and our days are productive. Passion is the guarantee that our lives will be exciting and full. Passion does not know boredom and never allows us to "kill time." To be passionate about something is to feel who we are and what we do has meaning.

My passion is helping people but reaches far beyond my own patients. I am tempted to say that I feel it is an obligation, although it is not one that annoys or burdens me. Instead, it excites and delights me. Passion is one of the central factors in setting the trajectory of my professional practice. Perhaps it would help if you could see each of the key factors laid out in order.

VISION: Had I never learned that the poor health of many is affected by what goes on in their brains as well as their bodies, and that all physical illnesses and injuries affect the mind and are affected by what goes on in the mind, I would have never discovered the healing that comes through treating the mind as well as the body simultaneously. Through years of research, Stephen Porges has shown the crucial role the vagus nerve performs in mental and physical health, and why one is always related to the other. Knowing the superior service I was able to provide my patients by treating their fears, despair, obsessions, and anxieties as well as their wounds and illnesses, opened my eyes to a hidden resource that could revolutionize health care.

PASSION: Once I began to treat my patients' minds as well as their bodies, the improved outcomes that we saw was evidence that what I had learned about the mind-body interaction was fact not fiction. I have always enjoyed helping others, but when the care I gave to my patients became more effective, my practice became more exciting and fascinating. My passion often became the unrelenting desire to share with many doctors and patients the benefits discovered through treating the whole person.

MISSION: This book is one example of my mission. I would like to see family practice physicians, other primary care physicians and mid-level practitioners such as PAs and NPs, as well as specialists, study and become familiar with the psychotropic medications that are available today. That may sound like a tall order, but every Doctor of Medicine or primary care provider has the background to understand the human nervous system and should be able to quickly digest the information regarding how a particular medication can affect specific neurotransmitters to produce specific effects. Pharmaceutical companies provide much of the information needed for doctors to decide which ones may be most helpful for each individual patient, though they cannot talk about "off label" benefits that are often better than what they are allowed to advertise. Each year more psychotropic medications are developed with ever more specific targets, so that patients can realize the benefits of the medication without having to suffer unnecessary side effects.

Part one of my mission is informing and equipping practitioners, especially primary care. Part two is getting the essence of mind-body healthcare to patients which is, basically, everyone. One concern is to enable patients to have intelligent conversations with their doctors so that their care becomes a collaboration, not a blind submission to an authority figure. Of course, patients do not need to know everything a doctor has to know, but it's not difficult to learn the basics.

Another concern is to have patients request this kind of care from their doctors rather than being referred to a psychiatrist, which is commonly done by practitioners when they do not feel comfortable treating these disorders.

This can place a financial burden on patients if they do not have insurance since psychiatrists are often quite expensive. There is no reason for not treating these disorders since it's easy to learn and exciting to witness the results firsthand. I do not mean to disparage psychiatrists who are necessary for true psychiatric emergencies, hospitalizations, more complex patients, and for those who need certain types of psychotherapy.

The Light That Now Shines

If I ignored the first glimmers of a new approach to treating patients that involved the integration of mind and body, if I had not sought to better understand the value of working with psychotropic medications to address physical ailments as well as destabilizing mental states, if I had not aggressively stayed on this path with dogged determination, I could have avoided a great deal of painful loss, slander, expense, and mountains of extra work. But then I would have betrayed myself, my patients, and many others who have benefitted and will benefit from The Corona Protocol as word of it spreads increasingly further.

I do not believe I could have lived with myself had I not pressed forward when light fell on the truths that began to appear in front of me. If I was driven at times—Denise would say all the time—it was because the knowledge of being one step away from a breakthrough method of treatment would mean a new and better life for thousands, perhaps millions of people.

It didn't have to be me doing all the work necessary to find the answers. It was never a competition or a need for recognition. The discovery of medical solutions to any problem we had until now that we had not been able to resolve is a wonderful thing regardless of who gets us there.

Any doctor whose entire career is focused on getting patients back to their best health and experience of well-being lives by the same determination that's driven me. I'll fight for what I believe is possible.

The dark times have become surprising gifts. What I've endured has increased my empathy, enlarged my perspective, and improved my work on behalf of others. When I tell a patient "I know how you feel, I've been there myself," they can look in my eyes and see I am telling the truth and feel I really understand.

Working at fulfilling a lifetime dream is not for the faint of heart, but running after one's dreams is something everyone should do.

People who are easily overwhelmed can be helped to build endurance and stamina. People who cannot see a future for their dream can be helped to a larger perspective, a perspective in which failures lead to success, weakness becomes strength, and slander helps to define and improve character. I am living proof of what I profess. Each day I'm grateful to God for holding onto me and my family through to the other side of what seemed would be my ruin but became a blessing.

What a wonderful relief I experienced in the summer of 2020 when my probation ended. I was nearing the end of this book, began a regular podcast "The Dr. Paul Show", and launched my new website with a social media campaign.

I'm looking forward to the future and all the possibilities with as much excitement as I've ever known.

I completed all the requirements after five more years of probation with no restrictions on my license. The year 2020 ended up being the most bizarre year in American (and world) history.

Challenges can lead to great opportunities and rewards. There was an opportunity to make a real difference, since I observed and felt a massive amount of suffering for so many. It's been a burden, and at times I felt a heavy weight of responsibility, but I believe it will be worth it.

We cannot see the good that can come from adversity before it hits, or in its first pain and setbacks. However, we can adopt beliefs and attitudes that enable us to endure hardship by getting to the other side with whatever benefits have come through the dark valleys. We do not control the future, nor can we predict what awaits. But we can hold onto our visions and the principles that sustain us in pursuing them.

I've tried passing my life lessons to my children, and the virtue of never allowing anything to get in the way of our visions that call us, our passions that drive us, and our missions that define us as humans whose lives will make a difference in the world.

All that's happened to me has humbled me, yet made me, emptied me, yet filled me, broken me, yet made me whole. This is my message to everyone.

Why not cooperate with life's unpredictable challenges and unprecedented opportunities so we can maximize the potential to be whole people and agents of change for the good of others and our world?

I'd be incredibly remiss if I didn't give a great deal of credence and gratitude to my wife, my two children, my father and Chuck. They are the earthly Angels in my life. Having their loving support during those difficult years made all the difference in the world.

I chalked it up to the risk of doing this job, but I knew it was worth it. With great risks come great rewards.

I smile as I think of my other love of my life who gives me such a sense of peace and relaxation—my little muse, best friend and beloved cat Seymour, my strikingly handsome seal point Himalayan. Best cat ever. Of course, our adorable dog JG is the other love of our family. They make us laugh each day and they're both completely spoiled. I look forward to the future celebrations we'll share as my dreams come to fruition.

ACKNOWLEDGEMENTS

First and foremost I would like to thank my pastor, mentor and friend Chuck Smith Jr. He has been with me since the beginning of my writing journey, which stared 20 years ago. He edited my first three books, and has edited and written certain parts of this book. He has been with me during the most difficult times, as well as the good times. Chuck, I am eternally grateful to you.

Thank you to Black Château Enterprises for marketing the book. Desireé Duffy and her terrific team have helped with marketing, PR, my website, and project management. My lead editor John Palisano did an incredible job. Everyone at BCE has been a pleasure to work with.

Thank you to Kathy Dunn for terrific cover design, as well as her assistant, Hobie Hobart.

Thank you to John Kremer for naming the book and for his sage advice when needed.

Thank you to Karen Corriente for formatting the book.

Acknowledgements

Thank you to my webmaster Jaine Simon and my IT consultant Derrick Low.

I am also grateful for the pharmaceutical companies that created these amazing medications which have been powerful tools to work with in order to create my protocol. I'm also thankful for the pharmaceutical reps who not only supply me with valuable samples but who also have become friends.

Thank you to my incredible assistant Leslie Perez, who makes my life easier. I would like to also acknowledge my previous assistants Fabiola Baltazar and Esther Lopez.

Last, I want to thank my family, friends, and patients who have all been an essential part of the journey of my life.

Made in the USA
Las Vegas, NV
09 August 2024

93587849R00174